Arnewood

ARNEWOOD

The Story of an Iowa Dairyman

By MELVIN SCHOLL

THE STATE HISTORICAL SOCIETY OF IOWA
IOWA CITY 1954

SF
33
.S3
A3

PRINTED IN THE UNITED STATES OF AMERICA
BY THE TORCH PRESS, CEDAR RAPIDS, IOWA

Editor's Foreword

THE STORY of dairying in Iowa in many ways parallels the history of dairying in the United States. Very few high-grade cattle could be found in the original thirteen colonies. True, the Dutch brought Holsteins into New Netherland, but these animals soon became mixed with poorer stock and gradually this bloodline disappeared. Short-horns were brought into Virginia, Maryland, and New York before 1800. Three decades later, about the time the Black Hawk Purchase was opened to settlement in 1833, an importing company brought many Shorthorns into Ohio. About this same time Guernseys were brought into New Hampshire. Stockmen began importing Jerseys into the Eastern states around 1850. Prior to the Civil War practically all of the Ayrshire cattle in the United States were held within the confines of New England, with Massachusetts probably having the greatest number. Some Herefords were to be found in this country before the Civil War, but they first attracted attention at the Philadelphia Centennial Exposition of 1876.

In view of the above facts it is not surprising that the Federal Census of 1840 does not list any dairy cattle in Iowa or, for that matter, in the nation. According to the Census of 1840 more swine were raised on Iowa farms than any other kind of livestock, probably to consume the corn and provide pork and lard for domestic use. The census takers counted 104,899 hogs and only 38,049 "neat cattle," 15,354 sheep, and 10,794 horses and mules.

Despite their omission from the Federal Census dairy cattle were highly prized, especially by the Midwestern pioneers. Illustrative of this fact is the following incident in the life of Nancy Ann Hunter, the mother of Henry Dodge, first governor of the Territory of Wisconsin, who lies buried beside his illustrious son, Augustus Caesar Dodge, in a Burlington cemetery. During Revolutionary War days fifteen-year-old Nancy Ann was living with her parents in western Kentucky. Indians had been attacking the settlers, and Nancy Ann and her parents had been obliged to flee to a nearby stockade for safety. As Louis Pelzer relates in his *Henry Dodge*:

> Such was the situation when one day a favorite cow gave birth to a calf a short distance from the fort. Both animals were exposed to the danger of capture by the skulking warriors; and so the settlers held a hurried consultation. But realizing the danger from hidden Redskins, none of them would venture outside. Then it was that alone and unaided Nancy Ann rushed forth and seized the calf in her arms, while all eyes were fixed upon her. Carrying the calf toward the fort, with the cow closely following after, she advanced toward the stockade while a volley of arrows whistled around her. Amid the joy of those in the fort all three reached the stockade unharmed.

The pioneers brought their own dairy cows with them into the Black Hawk Purchase. According to John B. Newhall the great thoroughfares of Indiana and Illinois "would be literally lined with long blue wagons of the emigrants slowly wending their way over the broad prairies — the cattle and hogs, men and dogs, and frequently women and children, forming the rear of the van — often ten, twenty, and thirty wagons in company. Ask them, when and where you would, their destination was the 'Black Hawk Purchase'."

Even the military forces on the Iowa frontier had their own dairy cows. Thus, in the spring of 1835 Colonel Stephen Watts Kearny was leading his United States Dragoons on an expedition along the watershed which divides the Des Moines and Skunk rivers. In his story of the expedition William J. Petersen records:

By the time they had reached the present site of Oskaloosa the weather had changed and the dragoons found themselves traversing prairies "covered with strawberries" in such abundance "as to make the whole track red for miles." Marching at the rate of about fifteen miles a day, the ripening of the strawberries coincided with their progress and gave them "this luxury for many weeks, increased by the incident of one of our beeves becoming a milker."

John B. Newhall was high in his praise of the dairy cow. In his *Sketches of Iowa,* printed in 1841, Newhall writes:

A cow, in the spring, is worth from 18 to 20 dollars, sometimes 25 dollars; the quality and richness of the milk is not surpassed in any country. From the springing up of grass until fall, butter is made in profusion, and generally sells from 12 to 18 cents per pound. Late in the autumn, the cows range further from the settlements, and from their irregularity in coming up for milking, are apt to go dry, which enhances the price of butter from 25 to $37\frac{1}{2}$ cents per pound; although a trifling effort will enable any farmer, with two or three good cows, to have abundance of fresh butter and milk in seasons of the greatest scarcity. The dairy business has not, as yet, been extensively gone into, although no country in the Valley of the Mississippi is better adapted for this lucrative pursuit, and none offer better inducements for markets.

John G. Wells was equally impressed with the possibilities of dairying in Iowa. In his *Pocket Hand-Book of Iowa: Past, Present, and Prospective,* which was printed in New York in 1857, Wells records:

The Dairy is another source of very profitable investment — there being a great deficiency in the requisite supply of dairy products throughout the state. It is said that at least one-half the grain now raised is exported, while twice the quantity of butter and five times the quantity of cheese required, is imported. The editor of the *Iowa Farmer* is so fully of the opinion that the dairy offers to the farmer a never-failing source of wealth, that he declares, were he possessed of the means, he would rather invest them in that channel than in any other branch of husbandry.

If the exhibits of milk cows at the first Iowa State Fairs are of any significance, there was little reason for Mr. Wells's optimism. During those early years milk cows were rarely exhibited at the State Fair. The following report on "Class 7" was made in the *Proceedings of the Iowa State Agricultural Society* after the second State Fair held at Fairfield in 1855.

This class, devoted to Milch Cows was not at all represented. The list of premiums required that a trial should be made of the quantity of milk, and of butter given and made from each cow during a certain specified time, and that a statement should be made certifying to the qualities, accuracy of the trial, &c. This of course, would take a great deal of trouble and attention; but the facts are important, and are worth far more than would compensate for all the trouble. In other States, such statements are furnished, and the results are published, proving a source of great value to all who read them. In this State, famous for its grazing purposes — famous for its butter and cheese, possessing all the advantages of the dairy with none of its disadvantages, we can beat the world; all that is necessary to prove this, is for you to make the trial next year. Competition in this department would add very much to the general interest of the Fair, would be highly creditable to exhibitors, and would certainly develop the resources of our farmers in this regard.

The same apathy was registered by Iowa dairymen when the State Fair was held at Dubuque in the opening days of the Civil War. In his "History of the Fair" published in the Dubuque *Daily Herald* and reprinted in the *Eighth Report of the Iowa State Agricultural Society,* Mr. C. Childs records:

It seems there was no farmer who would show a yoke of oxen for $10. Nor would any one show a milch cow for the premium of $20, nor compete for a second premium of $10. If there be any good cows in this part of the State next year it would be commendable for somebody to take those premiums. It is said, however, perhaps with some propriety, that the requirements in reference to the trial of weight and quantity of milk and amount of butter, for a specified time, and the affidavit of the facts, makes too much trouble in the matter. Would it not be well to have the competing cows milked at the time of the Fair and the butter made by some exhibitor of a churning machine, if practicable, so that during the occasional observations of two or three days the Committee could form a tolerably correct estimate of the merits for a premium?

Actually, little progress was made in dairying in Iowa during the 1860's. A few small local dairies gradually sprang up but they were relatively unimportant both from the standpoint of quality and quantity. It remained for John Stewart to bring Iowa to a position of leadership in the dairy industry.

Born in Ohio in 1836, John Stewart had served in the Union army throughout the Civil War. In 1866 he became a jobber in butter, cheese, and farm produce at St. Louis. The work must have appealed to him, for in 1867 he engaged in the same business at Galena. Moving to Manchester in 1870, Stewart started a creamery a few miles east of that thriving little community in 1872. His Spring Branch Creamery is said to have been the first butter creamery in Iowa.

At that time eastern dairymen held western products in low repute: they not only scoffed at the poor breeding of Iowa cattle, but they questioned the ability and honesty of all western dairymen. According to C. A. Huston of Waubeek "our butter was universally known as Western grease, and our cheese as leatherback and white-oak."

Such a situation must have seemed intolerable to a man of John Stewart's character. Having won prizes for his butter at St. Louis, he determined to compete at the International Centennial Exposition at Philadelphia in 1876. The chances of this obscure Iowa man against the finest buttermakers of Europe and America must have seemed exceedingly slim, but the judges awarded the gold medal for the "best package of Butter exhibited" to John Stewart. This honor is said to have removed much of the "prejudice" against Iowa butter and was calculated to have added from $500,000 to $1,000,000 annually to the income of dairymen in the Hawkeye State.

Encouraged by Stewart's success, sixty-six dairymen convened at

Manchester on February 2, 1877, and organized the Northern Iowa Butter and Cheese Association. John Stewart was naturally elected president, and Robert M. Littler of Davenport was chosen secretary-treasurer. On account of the "general depression," only a few new names were added to the membership roll in 1878, but the officers were not discouraged. The third annual meeting, like the first two, was held at Manchester, which was becoming known as the "Elgin of Iowa." Despite "cold and stormy" weather, many dairymen attended from Iowa, Illinois, Kansas, Nebraska, and Dakota Territory. An eyewitness declared that the caliber of dairymen who packed Manchester city hall was "seldom equalled and never excelled." The membership of the association was increased to 190, and steps were taken to have Iowa products exhibited that summer at the Royal Agricultural Society International Fair at London.

The conventions of 1880 and 1881 were held at Monticello. At the Cedar Rapids meeting in 1882 the name of the association was changed to "The Iowa Butter and Cheese Association." Marshalltown entertained the dairymen in 1883 and Strawberry Point in 1884 and again in 1885.

The growing importance of Iowa as a dairy state was proved by the eleventh annual meeting of the association which was held at Manchester in 1887 in conjunction with the National Butter, Cheese and Egg Association. It was a proud day for Manchester and Delaware County. A committee of 110 members had been appointed to make "full and ample" arrangements for the 1,500 delegates. Representatives came from places as widely separated as New Hampshire and Colorado. President Schermerhorn called the convention to order and State Dairy Commissioner H. D. Sherman welcomed the guests. Speeches were made on almost every phase of agriculture and dairy-ing — a note of warning being sounded by David B. Henderson of Dubuque against the oleomargarine interests. The display of dairy machinery was exceptionally large.

The westward expansion of the dairy area in Iowa was attested by the meeting of the Iowa Butter and Cheese Association at Fort Dodge in 1890. At the fifteenth annual meeting at Waverly in 1891, the dairymen reorganized and adopted the name "Iowa State Dairy Association."

The position and prestige of dairying was greatly strengthened by the formation of this state association. In 1876, for example, the State Commission for the Philadelphia Centennial Exposition refused to allow a portion of their appropriation to be used for a dairy display, and John Stewart consequently had to finance his own exhibit. In 1904, on the other hand, the Iowa Commission to the Louisiana Purchase Exposition at St. Louis proudly reported: "The state displayed a map of large size showing the exact location of 792 creameries, together with other statistics; butter produced in the state for 1903, 140 million pounds, of which 77 million pounds were exported from the state. We had also in the same year 1,423,348 milch cows." Since Iowa had been awarded the highest butter scores at Philadelphia in 1876, at New Orleans in 1885, at Chicago in 1893, and at Omaha in 1898, the Commission felt it was incumbent upon her butter producers to "maintain the high excellence already attained." Unfortunately, Minnesota won first place at St. Louis, but Iowa could take pride in the fact that the second and third best tubs entered at St. Louis came from the Hawkeye State.

Although Iowa had made giant strides since the days of John Stewart in '76, a note of warning was sounded by E. R. Shoemaker of Waterloo in 1908. Almost any farmer could herd cattle profitably on five-dollar land, he declared, but could it be done when land sold at $100 or $150 an acre? Shoemaker urged economy in two directions: first, by the erection of silos to save the forty million dollars wasted in corn stalks; second, by the improvement of the dairy stock. Iowa was twenty years behind as a dairy section, for her 1,500,000 dairy cattle produced an average of only 140 pounds of butterfat yearly. In Europe dairy cows averaged 300 pounds of butterfat annually. Shoemaker estimated that Iowa dairymen were losing from twenty to thirty million dollars a year because of poor cows and archaic methods.

It was this situation as well as the small attendance which prompted the officers of the Iowa State Dairy Association to adopt President W. B. Barney's suggestion to hold a dairy cow exhibition in conjunction with their regular meeting at Cedar Rapids in 1909. About twenty-five cattle were exhibited: Holsteins by W. B. Barney and Frank White of Hampton; Jerseys by C. T. Graves of Maitland, Missouri; Ayrshires by Iowa State College; and Guernseys by a local breeder. During the four-day convention Professor Hugh G. Van

Pelt gave demonstrations of the good and bad points of dairy cattle, using the stock on exhibition for illustrative purposes. This was the "first time that anything of this nature" had been done and the "extreme interest" created stamped the Cedar Rapids dairy show as a real success.

Out of such humble beginnings grew the Waterloo Dairy Cattle Congress, which held its first meeting on October 10, 1910, with some 300 Holstein, Jersey, Guernsey, and Ayrshire cows on exhibition. The Brown Swiss were soon added and have become one of the stellar attractions. Meanwhile, the Dairy Congress has grown into one of the outstanding shows in the United States with fully 970 cattle exhibited at the Silver Jubilee in 1934. The number of cattle shown since that date frequently tops this impressive figure, as Iowans enter their prize animals against the best in the country.

Between 1850 and 1940 the average dairy cow in Iowa has increased its production from 147.9 gallons of milk to 556 gallons. The latter figure is only an average, for superior cows enrolled in herd-improvement associations were producing an average of 947 gallons. This increase has been attributed by C. Y. Cannon, Professor of Dairy Husbandry at Iowa State College, "to more extensive use of purebred dairy cattle, especially high quality dairy bulls, and to the elimination of unprofitable animals." As one looks back over the century the influence of the Iowa State Agricultural Society, the State Fair, the Iowa State Improved Breeders' Association, the Waterloo Dairy Congress and kindred organizations must become apparent to all.

In the present volume the author has presented a sympathetic and graphic account of the tremendous amount of personal care, knowledge, and attention required of a successful dairy farmer. Happily, the Hawkeye State is blessed with many outstanding dairymen. Little wonder that Iowa's 1,076,000 dairy cows produced nearly 5 per cent of the nation's milk in 1953.

WILLIAM J. PETERSEN

Superintendent and Editor
State Historical Society of Iowa
Iowa City, Iowa

Author's Preface

THE FIRST part of this book was written many years ago as a separate
and complete story. It was one of those first feeble attempts at writing that usually — and happily — end up in the wastebasket — and
in this case actually did. Nor was it the last of my earlier literary
pieces marked for the same untimely and cruel grave. Later, however,
when the present narrative evolved, it was felt most suitable to incor-
porate the original story in the present work; in fact, the germ plot
of *Arnewood* can be traced to the story of many years ago that just
could not be consigned to oblivion.

My own personal interest in the subject material will be so much
in evidence to the reader, once he begins my story, that it would

hardly seem necessary to dwell on that aspect of it here. My one wish is to impart this understanding of the dairy cow to the reader.

I am deeply indebted to many persons in one way or another for making _The Story of an Iowa Dairyman_ as attractive and appealing a finished product as is possible. First, the debt I owe Mrs. Jessie B. Piersol, former principal of Rockwell Public High School and Grinnell College alumna, for giving me many hours of inspirational guidance and tutoring in those subjects an aspiring writer is most in need of in her own home after school hours and with no thought of compensation — this debt is a very real one. Too often, alas, good teachers receive inadequate recognition for their invaluable services.

I wish also to mention the generous help of Dr. Grace Hunter, of the English Department of Grinnell College, who worked along with me in a critical way throughout the first drafts of the manuscript.

Others whose assistance in preparing and publishing the present volume is hereby gratefully acknowledged include Mrs. Harold Wolcott, Rockwell, Iowa, who aided in research with the chapter on threshing; Mr. M. M. Campbell, Newton, Iowa, who patiently read both the manuscript and the galley proofs, offering excellent criticisms, and also very generously supplying many of the fine pictures used in illustrating the book; and to Dr. William J. Petersen, superintendent of the State Historical Society of Iowa, not only for his fine introduction to the story, but for his support and assistance throughout every phase of preparing the manuscript for publication. Finally, I deeply appreciate the fine editorial assistance of Dr. Mildred Throne and Dr. Leola N. Bergmann.

Grateful acknowledgment is here made to the following for their permission to use some of their material in the preparation of this book — the Holstein-Friesian Association of America, Brattleboro, Vermont; Dr. W. E. Petersen of the University of Minnesota; and Mr. Merton Moore of the Carnation Milk Farms, Seattle, Washington.

Last but not least my sincere thanks and indebtedness to the black and white cow herself who inspired these pages and to whom they are respectfully dedicated.

MELVIN SCHOLL

Contents

Illustrations

Part One

A Boy and His Cow

Cutie

ONE Sunday afternoon in early August in 1930, when I was a mere lad of thirteen, an event occurred which was destined to influence great decisions throughout my life. It had become a regular Sunday custom in our home to go out for a drive to see the farm my father had purchased; but on this particular Sunday afternoon, instead of driving on to the farm as usual, my father stopped at a pasture he had leased just outside of town, in which his cattle were kept during the summer months. I thought he wanted to make sure the cows had a supply of salt or to see how the grass was "holding out." I noticed a peculiar twinkle in his eyes, however, which was a singular expression of his when trying to conceal a surprise he had planned for someone. I knew, too, with a glance at my mother, that she was a partner in the conspiracy, and I was instantly filled with excitement.

"Come on, kids," Father said, as he left the car and headed for the pasture fence. "Better keep Roselyn and Eldena in the car with you, Jo," he called back to my mother.

Oliver had climbed over the front seat of the two-door coach and had scrambled out, falling headlong to the ground, before Judy and I could manage to get out. But he sprang up instantly, his face and hands and clothes covered with road dust, and ran like a deer toward Father, who was waiting for us by the fence. Holding one strand of barbwire down with his left foot, and the top wire up with his left hand, Father helped us through with his free hand.

We walked down toward the creek. The cattle, upon discovering our approach, suddenly stopped eating to look at us. The startled calves and yearlings, wide-eyed, their heads high, and their tails raised, dashed across the hummocks on the far side of the stream. The milch cows, deceived into believing it was milking time, sloshed into the cool water, pausing in the middle of the creek long enough to enjoy its refreshing sensations; then they started lazily up the bank toward us, with the old cow, Blackie, in the lead.

My father was of medium stature and very stoutly built, but middle age had already given him its "spread" around the belt. For this reason it was always more comfortable for him to allow his suit coat to remain unbuttoned and his paunch to stick out in all its voluptuousness. I believe he was rather proud of it, since he made no attempt to conceal it. This posture, with arms akimbo, was a typical one with him whenever he felt complete inward satisfaction or amusement. He was reveling in both of these feelings as he surveyed the herd of cows as they approached. Oliver had for the moment forgotten what matter of importance had brought us to the scene in his greater eagerness to scare the calves and yearlings. They would stop at a distance to turn back and eye us surreptitiously. My brother would then pick up small stones and toss them into the water near the young animals. The splashing in the stream would send them bounding again across the bogs.

My father turned to us abruptly and said, "I'm giving you each a cow for your own. You can pick out any one you want. I wish one of my boys to grow up and be a good farmer."

"Oh, Dad, you mean it — honest?" I cried joyfully. "I'd love to have old Blackie!"

"And I want Pet!" Judy exclaimed, dancing in the grass.

Pet was the veritable Amazon of the herd, a big roan cow, awkward, slow, and always contented. She required no fondling and remained indifferently attentive when any fuss was made over her. She had a powerful head which she enjoyed rubbing in the soft dirt, adorning her face in much the same manner as her two-legged sisters use a compact.

"Twinkletoes is mine!" Oliver said. Dropping a handful of stones, he ran up to the red and white cow and grasped her around the neck. The cow did not mind in the least, being a frivolous, fetching creature that responded more to human attentions than most cows do. Twinkletoes actually performed acrobatic feats when milking time came or whenever she had an opportunity to show off.

Father seemed well pleased with the selections and voiced this opinion; then, turning to me, said, "None of you has picked the best one in the herd, though." He paused a moment while he removed a cigar from his lapel pocket, and speculatively bit off the end. "Although I have refused several offers to sell her, I'm going to give the young Holstein heifer to you, Melvin, in place of Blackie. I know," he said, noticing the look of disappointment in my face, "Blackie is a mighty fine cow now, but she's getting old, and may never have another calf. Take the mischievous little heifer, son, and take my word for it, someday you'll own the best cow in Cerro Gordo County."

And so the wayward heifer fell into my possession. This heifer was a grade Holstein, and had just dropped her first calf that spring. My brother and I had always been afraid of her; indeed, we were willing to do anything around the house for Mother if she would milk this formidable bovine. The cow was, nonetheless, beautifully marked, possessed a pair of sparkling eyes (which were the principal cause of concern to Oliver and me), and, as if these were not enough endowments for one animal, she had a rounded, deep barrel of a middle, and a large well-attached udder.

Had I not been blinded as it were by my unreasonable terror of her, I would have recognized her then as the magnificent cow she later proved to be. I knew only that I feared those fiery eyes, which seemed to watch my every movement; feared that sleek, proud head of hers; feared every part of her. This aversion for the heifer seems foolish to me now, for she never actually hurt anyone; but her threats were so resolute that it appeared likely they would be carried out at any time.

The worst fault she had was her habit of walking away as soon as my brother or I sat down to milk her. The aggravating part of it was that she would stop at a short distance from us, turn her wicked eyes upon us, and wait for us to come up again; then the whole process would be repeated. I often thought she spent much of her time devising new methods of provocation.

The black and white heifer remained for the time being nameless and obscure. It is indeed a strange quirk in human nature that we find so much to love in something that belongs to us, so much goodness lost to us before the thing becomes our own. Sometimes an object of our deepest antipathy is changed into an object of our highest affection after it comes into our possession.

So it was with the young heifer that had become mine. From the moment my father gave her to me a new feeling for her was awakened in me. I was no longer afraid of her; instead, I felt myself admiring her as though I had seen her for the first time. The heifer herself must have been conscious of my changed feeling, because she responded to my attentions with the greatest docility. She would come up to me in the pasture and lick my hands with her rough tongue; then she would stand by, contentedly chewing her cud, while I brushed the flies away from her legs and belly with a green willow switch.

In time my pet became so devoted to her new master that no one else could milk her. She would raise her hind leg (either one was equally efficient) with such suddenness and dexterity as to catch the spurious milker unawares. This hoof bombardment, while failing narrowly in hitting its target, never failed, however, to advise anyone that the heifer wanted only her master's gentle touch.

I cannot say exactly when or why my pet arrived at her singular cognomen, but it was certainly sometime during that first summer when she was given to me that she received the name "Cutie." One had only to watch this ingenious little creature as she grazed with the rest of the herd or as she doted upon the many little attentions her young master bestowed upon her to realize how aptly the name suited her. It became so much a part of her that I could never again apply it to any animal but the black and white heifer.

One frosty October morning my brother and I helped Father drive the cows back to the farm for the winter. There I bade Cutie farewell and returned to my home in town where I spent that winter busily engaged in my high school studies. Not until the snows of winter had thawed and spring had come back did I see Cutie again. She was rather gaunt and her once lustrous black and white coat was soiled and shabby — the result of the long, bitter cold winter months spent in the stable. She was to calve in early July, a fact which explained the great decrease in her milk flow since I had last milked her. Another reason perhaps was the fact that it had become necessary to put hobbles on her legs in order to milk her. That had hurt her pride more than her legs, and Cutie would not give her milk down.

Though bovines are not capable of registering emotions on their faces in the same manner as people, nevertheless I knew Cutie was glad to see me. I had been worried for fear she might have forgotten me, but when I called her by name, she came running up to me as she always had done and began rubbing her clammy nose against my coat pocket in search of an ear of corn or an apple, her favorite desserts. This time it happened to be a big red apple. She was none too careful how she got to the choice morsel, so that my blue denim appendage was ever after incapable of serving its original purpose.

About this time a great depression was engulfing the entire country. At first it was only an abstruse term to us, a topic for discussion heard at almost every gathering; our happy home was as yet untouched by its destructive fingers. Farmers, one after another, were losing their farms. Prices for livestock and grain fell so low that there was no longer any profit in raising them. Corn was being burnt as fuel because coal was too high priced to buy. Oats were bought up by many of the wealthier farmers at eleven cents a bushel for speculation. Later, they resold the grain for eight cents. In protest against low prices for dairy products, some farmers who could stand it poured their whole milk into the hog troughs. The best milch cows could be purchased for $25. Only those few farmers who had their farms paid for and managed their affairs wisely could eke out of the land a decent existence. Men of the soil were, however, in most cases better off than those who lived in the cities. There was almost no work to be had. They might get a few days of work at a time for a dollar a day. Things went from bad to worse. One by one the banks began to close, and the meager life savings of old folks no longer able to work were lost.

In the midst of this chaos a new board of supervisors was elected in Cerro Gordo County. Previous to this time my father had had all the roads to build that he could handle; in fact, his territory had extended into adjoining Franklin County. With the new setup, however, everything was changed. Grading of county roads was let by contract, the lowest bidder getting the job. With this apportioning of road construction, which had already been cut severely because of the dwindling funds available in the county for this purpose, my father soon found himself without enough work to keep his crew of men busy. Because he had always been a good "credit risk" with both of the town's banks, he had grown to rely on his credit to keep him going steadily forward, with a minimum of cash on hand at any time. Whether or not this was in any way a reflection upon his injudicious business policies, it was nonetheless a popular disease of the times. Then, almost overnight the banks became wary of every customer. This, coupled with his own precarious position, brought my father's credit to an abrupt halt.

Father was a headstrong person. He knew how roads ought to be built, and he built them that way. When one of the new members of the board of supervisors began telling him how the roads should be constructed, with a view to economizing on the county funds, my father became furious.

"I've been building roads in this county all my life," he stormed at the supervisor, who had come out to inspect the work, "and if I do say so myself they're the finest roads anywhere, and I ain't going to start making some God-forsaken cow-roads just because you say so!"

"I ain't saying you're not the best road grader in these parts," the county official replied in a conciliatory tone, "but we have got to build cheaper roads than we have in the past. Perhaps soon we will not be able to build any at all." He continued, gesturing with his arm, "You can cut down on the yardage of dirt you're getting from the hill over there, and bring more of it from the fence-rows, and still make a good road. The shoulders don't have to be quite as high as you're getting them, Art."

My father eyed him silently for a minute as both men stood in the center of the road, filled now with fresh excavations of pungent black earth. Then he said callously, "You figure that'd be economizing. Well, I don't! That hill has got to be cut down to fill in the low places and to make the road level. The shoulders have got to be high. Heaven knows how these country roads fill in with snow during the winter. We can't make them too high. I've never built a road that a farmer couldn't mow all along its shoulders and ditches, and by damn I'm not going to start now!" With that he walked back to his machine, leaving the supervisor standing in the middle of the road.

The outcome of these misunderstandings was that my father eventually found himself without any work at all. Then, and only then, with awful portent, did the full meaning of the depression become known to us.

I remember one evening Father came home, his usually cheerful face haggard and worried. He had somehow aged, I thought; he was not the father I had known before. He pushed back his plate at the supper table, after touching only a little of the food upon it, and rising wearily went into the living room, where he fell heavily on the davenport. He seldom read the newspapers, but had always enjoyed having Judy read the front page to him while he rested after supper.

Mother had been watching him solicitously but had said nothing. She called into the living room to him now, and in a matter-of-fact voice which did not betray her own uneasiness, asked, "Do you want Judy to come in and read the news to you, Art?"

"No, I'm too tired tonight," he answered, almost in a whisper.

Mother continued to eat thoughtfully, then dropped her fork onto her plate and went into the other room where she sat down on the davenport beside her husband.

"You didn't get the bid again," she said softly after a time.

"No, I didn't," and his voice seemed far away.

"How bad is it?" my mother asked, looking wistfully at him. "I must know."

"Bad enough."

"What are we going to do?"

My father turned over so he would not have to face her, and he said hoarsely, "There is only one thing left to do: sacrifice the farm or this house."

"And you want to keep the farm?" she ventured the truth.

"I'll never give it up!"

"Then we shall give up our town house and move to the farm," Mother said tenderly. "I have had all I wanted here — in this house. I must be thankful for that." And only now can I realize how many memories must have been hers, and hers alone, in that house where she had reigned. But she was willing to give them all up in the face of disaster. By late spring it was finally decided that we would have to give up our home in town and move to the farm.

My father was not a farmer. I know that now. He was a genius with machines and roads, and it must have been a deathblow to sacrifice his tractors and graders. The roads were the only life he had known; he was as much a part of them as the automobiles and trucks that traversed their surfaces. My father had often taken us boys along with him during the summertime. My own health as a boy had been frail, and the doctor had instructed my father to keep me away from books and indoor study as much as possible.

The grease, the dirt, and the noise of the huge machines were most disagreeable to me. Sometimes I would ride on the grader with my father and watch him maneuver the wheels that raised or lowered the great blade cutting into the road ditch. Wheels also regulated the keel of the machine as one side passed on top of the grade while the other side rode in the ditch. At this dizzy angle I had to clutch desperately to the seat to keep from bouncing off as the big steel wheels rolled over the rocks and huge clumps of earth. A big Aultman-Taylor steam tractor pulled the grader back and forth over the road. The noise that it made as it chugged and strained for power to make a hill was deafening; then its steady, rumbling ping-ping as it slowly leveled off made my eyelids heavy as the fierce heat of the sun drove mercilessly down upon me. Later a Rumely Oil Pull tractor replaced the steam giant; still later a Caterpillar was purchased to pull a more up-to-date excavator.

I always liked the invigorating, pungent smell of freshly turned earth. I would watch the furrows of green sod roll up under me and fall bottom-side up until I became drowsy. A bevy of blackbirds followed the grader and lit on the moist black soil to snatch greedily for the worms and bugs uncovered by the blade. The dirt was first taken out of the ditches and fence-rows and piled high on the shoulder of the road until one might think, by viewing the process, that not even an animal could walk over the huge mass of debris piled on the road bed. Small hills were cut down and the dirt carried down into the low places. Rocks and tree-stumps were blasted out. The finished road was a marvel to see, straight and black, level and fine, with shoulders that were high and symmetrical.

My brother always rode with the cat skinner (a term applied to the tractor driver), and when he became restless and jumped off I would do the same, and we would go off by ourselves to explore the countryside. Sometimes one of the farmers let us use his Shetland ponies, and we would ride for hours until we were so sore we could hardly sit down to eat our dinner.

Life for all of us was changed completely when we moved to the small farm. In losing all contacts with small town life and moderate pretensions to luxury, I was introduced to nature in the raw. I belonged to the farm, I knew, and though there have been times in later life when I was forced to live away from it, I never forgot it. There is too much of it in me now ever to shake it off, and I am glad.

The "forty" comprised some of the best soil in Cerro Gordo County. Until my father had purchased it, the entire farm had been virgin soil, never having felt the touch of the plow lathe, but rather having slept for centuries undisturbed save by gentle interruptions of grazing animals and primitive tribes of Indians. Its soil had been preserved and enriched with each passing year. One of the greatest phenomena of nature ever witnessed was to watch the corn that grew on that land those first years when it was turned over and put into cultivation. You could almost see the tiny green shoots of corn growing. By comparison one had only to watch the neighbors' fields of corn just across the fence. Only as I grew older did I realize the importance of conserving this fertility for generations yet unborn.

The farm lay on the south side of a fine graveled road, just midway between Mason City and Rockwell. A small, almost dilapidated house was set off from the road among a thin grove of box elders. A double corncrib and a small barn huddled together in the background, with a little milkhouse, a stock tank, and a windmill squeezed in between them.

This was the way the place looked on that July morning in 1932 when I realized that it was to be my new home, the second one I had ever known. How was I to know then what deep memories that little farm was to leave in me, memories that even now grow so real and so persistent that I long to be back there. To the east I saw a small meadow of green alfalfa, waving in purple bloom. South of that, and extending to the southwest of this perspective, a field of corn, more than knee-high, waved its verdant crests in the southern breeze. West of the buildings, past a row of stately, scarred poplar trees, an expanse of grass like a beautiful sea of mystic colors stretched to the skyline.

Beneath the trees in the foreground the cows jostled each other to keep away the swarm of flies that would follow them incessantly during the long hot summer months. One animal there I saw, a black and white creature, that stood out among all the others. The picture was new for me, unforgettable. It was lovely. It was home, and for me Cutie was the center, the joy of it all.

II

Learning to Be a Dairyman

ONE morning in July when I opened the stable door to let the cows in for milking, Cutie was not with the herd. For one agonizing moment I thought something terrible had happened to her. Even though the heifer had been dry for about six weeks now, she had always been the one to rush through the barn door to occupy the first stanchion. I called to her now by name, and in answer there came from the direction of the west pasture a low, almost calf-like cry — a plaintive, almost human sound that I could distinguish from all others. In her

13

own way she was telling me she could not come. In that instant I guessed what had happened!

My whole being was trembling with excitement and anticipation. The thing I had been waiting for so long was taking place. Cutie was having a calf, and a new thrill and hope obsessed me. Could it possibly be a heifer calf? For that was what I wanted so badly.

I rushed down the crooked cowpath as fast as my legs would take me. I did not stop to notice the heavy dew on the tall grass in the pasture, or the young brood of pheasants that I had scared into flight. Over a rise of ground, carefully selected by the heifer for dropping her calf away from all other life, I found Cutie standing over her newborn calf, maternally licking away the wet membrane that covered her sprawling offspring. She nuzzled my hands when I approached, to make certain I was no enemy. Satisfied, she resumed her vigorous massaging. How proud she was of the calf! And my heart suffered a quick pang of revolt at the thought that in a few days her baby would be taken from her. My pity for the calf, however, was short lived upon discovering it to be a bull.

I was fascinated by this miracle of new life. The heifer was nervously attentive to the actions of her almost helpless young, and emitted low anxious cries each time the calf attempted to get to its feet. I could not help laughing at the little wobbly creature as it stumbled to its feet, swaying for a moment on its four spindly limbs, braced like a sawhorse, then losing all control and falling headlong to the ground. Undaunted, it would try again and again, finally succeeding in remaining upright long enough to take a step. Its first instinct was one of hunger, and it began searching for food, which meant the dam's udder and the rich colostrum it contained. It was a difficult job indeed to synchronize its sense of balance and space, keeping all four feet under it and at the same time reaching for one of the teats. For some time the teat seemed to bobble away from its mouth like an apple on a string; then, almost by accident the little pink mouth encircled it, and the first food began to ooze down the calf's throat, and with the first pleasurable thrills accompanying the new taste the hunger became more intense. He bumped her udder in protest to the slowness with which the liquid trickled down his throat, and the mother raised her leg in mild reproach. Cutie turned around to lick the calf's buttocks, and as it gorged its baby stomach with the milk from its own mother, its little tail kept switching like a grenadier's plume.

With this, her second calf, Cutie had developed an udder of great promise. The swelling in it was very great, as is usually the case in first- and second-calf heifers. Several times each day I milked the sticky, golden milk from the heifer's udder to alleviate the inflammation in it.

Oliver wanted to call the calf Billie, and as I did not greatly mind, that was its name. When I took Billie away from his mother and put him in a pen with Hulda, a heifer calf from one of the other cows, Cutie could not understand and bellowed for her baby all day and all night. She would not go out to the pasture and eat. If it had not been for my father, I would surely have given the calf back to Cutie, but he kept telling me she would soon forget about the little fellow. Even animals have to make great sacrifices, I thought.

Now began the arduous task of teaching the calf to drink from a pail. At first Billie was obstinate and refused to drink; but his hunger got the best of him, and when the pail of milk was brought to him the second time, he greedily took my finger and sucked up the milk. Sometimes he was so impatient he would butt the pail between my legs, spilling milk over my overalls. After finishing such a meal, Billie would run over to Hulda and suck her ears until they looked like two drowned rats.

Cutie was heavy now at the pail, and in a short time ceased calling for her calf. As the summer days passed I overcame, in a measure, my disappointment in the bull calf in the pleasure I derived from playing with it. Billie did not look at all like his mother. Having been sired by a Black Angus, his coat was all black. He had, nevertheless, his mother's fetching ways. He loved more to be fondled by us children than to frisk with Hulda on the grass.

Before long two more cows freshened, and little Hulda was sold to make room in the pen for the new calves. Billie resented the change. Perhaps he felt a bit too grown-up to suckle their ears, or else he was irritated when they reached for his.

From this time on, Cutie kept apart from the rest of the herd, always waiting for me to come to her. Seldom now was she seen grazing with the other cows. Cutie seemed to enjoy her little world more fully than most cows do, and gloated over the special attention she received from her young owner. Day after day was much the same with her. She walked through the green grass, stopped to eat what she wanted of it, drank deeply of the cool water from the tank, or stood under the shade of the trees, lazily allowing the chickens and ducks to pick the flies from her legs and belly. Sometimes the fowls had to make little jumps to reach the flies under her belly, but Cutie never stepped on any of them. Sometimes she sank down on the matted ground beneath the trees, and with silent complacency chewed her cud, always drinking in life to its fullest measure. The grass, the water, the trees, the air, and the sky were hers to enjoy during the daylight hours; then, when her udder became painfully full of the rich, life-giving milk, I would come to bring her quick relief as she stood with her tail resting neatly in a wide arc over her rump. Occasionally a fly would bite especially hard, and her tail would leave its restful attitude, descending in a mad swoop upon the tiny demon.

"You just keep that tail of yours out of my face, Cutie," I warned her, and as if she understood what I was saying, she flipped her tail around my neck for a dead ringer, and there it would stay until another fly made her forget all her ladylike manners.

The only time Cutie did not obey me was when she found the gate to the cornfield open and slipped through. This was the one forbidden fruit that grew in her garden of paradise, and as surely as Eve realized her guilt, just as surely did Cutie know that she was sinning. But the temptation was so delightful and the demon inside of her so insidious, that Cutie could no more control herself than she could fly. The stalks of corn crushed beneath her feet, and the ears snapped as her hungry jaws gulped them down. Finally I would discover the villain and try to walk up to her with cajoling words. Off she would go, breaking more corn down in her path. Fear became greater than my impatience with her, and I would shout to her to stop.

"Cutie, come here! If Dad finds out you've been in the corn, you'll hear from him, and so will I! You come back here!"

This game of hide-and-seek went on until by some stealthy maneuvering I managed to take her by surprise during one of those brief, ecstatic moments when the little gourmand had an ear of corn poised in her mouth for the pleasurable process that would make it ready for its quick journey down the chute to the storeroom. I grabbed her around the neck, and at that instant I was her conqueror. She followed me out of the field merely by my taking hold of one of her ears. For the size of her head, Cutie's ears were dreadfully out of proportion, and I fear this using them as a halter aided very materially in pulling them out of shape.

MELVIN SCHOLL
After Dispersal in 1951

Aerial View of Arnewood Farm — Cerro Gordo County

August came and went. The aftermath of alfalfa sent its tangy scent across the fields, and the corn stood shocked in the southwest field like rows of Indian wigwams. September came and with it the first signs of an early fall — a landscape of red, yellow, and russet. The lowing of the cows as they waited to be milked, the bawling of the calves for their supper, the creaking of the windmill wheel turning with the brisk wind that rustled through the leaves of the poplar trees, and the whirring of a tractor in a distant field were sounds that become inseparable from the vivid picture memory paints of the old forty of yesterday.

Had Cutie been a Jersey or a Guernsey instead of a Holstein, it is an almost certain fact that I should now be a Jersey or a Guernsey enthusiast. It was, therefore, quite by accident that I became acquainted with the breed of dairy cattle now universally accepted as the leader both in milk and in butterfat production.

My association with this breed was further secured by the fact that at this time my nearest neighbor was a veteran breeder of purebred Holstein-Friesian cattle; his herd was acknowledged as one of the finest in the state. I learned much invaluable knowledge about dairying through several years of close contact with this master farmer and dairyman, H. J. Schlichting. A great deal of my success from the start was made possible by the help and cooperation of this man.

Like so many of the great Americans of today, Mr. Schlichting came to this country from Germany as a boy, with nothing in his possession but those staunch principles learned from parents who were close to their Maker; a realization of the value of good farming made real by the necessity of earning a livelihood for a large family on a few acres in the Old World; and an indomitable will to succeed.

The fertile soil of Iowa beckoned to this young man. The opportunities at that time were great, and the years following the first World War were good to him. He married and his dreams and hopes reached their fruition in a family of two sons and three daughters, and a fortune that at forty might have been sufficient to allow him and his family comfort for the rest of their lives.

It was only natural, however, that a man with his determination should be restless in such a quiescent state of affairs. Besides, the times were such as afforded great inducements for making fabulous fortunes in land. Mr. Schlichting sold his extensive holdings near Klemme, Iowa, and invested heavily in lands both in north-central Iowa and in the Dakotas, making only the required down payments. He moved with his family to Klemme, where his wife might have it easier and his children might go to town school.

Then the land boom was over. Suddenly and mercilessly, misfortune struck from all sides. Tenants on his farms moved out at night, leaving Mr. Schlichting without paying their rent. One farm after another was lost. The entire property in the Dakotas was liquidated and sunk in a small hotel in an out-of-the-way town in South Dakota. Then the government stepped in to collect income taxes on land that was sold. The money was gone, and he could not settle with the government.

His wife, always his strong right arm, became ill at this time. Her malady was of a rare nature. Though financial conditions were already strained, the good man took his ailing wife to all parts of the country, hoping that a cure might be effected. A paralysis was slowly gripping the woman, and everywhere doctors could only shake their heads. Even then the man did not give up. She was taken to the hospital at Iowa City. The same negative response. Then to the Mayo Clinic at Rochester, Minnesota, the most famous of its kind in the world. Again no hope. At last the loving husband took his wife back to Iowa to face ruin and despondency.

There was one small farm left in Cerro Gordo County with a heavy mortgage on it, the little hotel in the Dakotas, and a wife who was to be confined to a wheel chair for twenty years before she was to find relief in death. All that time she was to remain completely helpless and dumb. He had five small children whom he must not fail. Henry Schlichting had a brother who always stood by with a helping hand. He took over the mortgage on the farm so that Henry could move on it. The hotel could not be sold, but a deal was worked out in which it was traded for fourteen head of purebred Holsteins. With this fresh start the stout-hearted man began once more from the bottom, and at fifty-five was on top again with a fine herd of cattle.

At this point I became acquainted with the man and his family. With such a background in the Old Country and such experience of misfortune in this, it is little wonder that his ideas about the tilth of the soil should be so exacting, his methods of husbandry so diligently practiced. There was no time lost on his well-kept and productive farm. From sunrise till sunset he and his children worked. His youngest son, Fred, stayed by his father and in the years that followed

entered into partnership with him. The eldest daughter, Lydia, had
to quit school when she was but ten years of age to take care of her
mother, to keep house, and to raise her younger sisters. She was en-
dowed by nature with a keen sense of values and with that indefinable
something that enabled her to make a house a home; these magnan-
imous qualities made up for her lack of schooling.

Some of the farmers in the neighborhood spent much of their time
"farmin' the road," and spending their money in town. These same
farmers had to cut their grain on Sundays, a procedure frowned upon
by Mr. Schlichting. He believed in working six days a week and giving Sunday to the Lord. In my many years of friendship with this
man I have never known him to work a single Sunday, nor to eat one
meal without first asking the blessing of the Giver of all sustenance.

Mr. Schlichting hired me to work for him by the day whenever
there were oats and corn to shock, hay to put up, or any number of
the many things that need to be done on a well-regulated dairy farm.
I deemed it a privilege to be allowed to help with the milking. How
I wished that I could own a string of such fine cattle!

"I would rather you took a little more time with your work," he
would say, "and do it well, than to work fast and not do it right."

The alfalfa was always cut at medium blossom stage, and only as
much mowed down at one time as could be put up without too much
risk of getting rained on. The soybeans that were to be cut for hay
were cocked into miniature pyramids; the oats were shocked in such a
way as to allow the sun and wind to penetrate them. If the season was
rainy or Mr. Schlichting was to be one of the last on the threshing
run, then the shocks of oats had to be capped.

One day while Fred and I were taking a rest from cocking soybeans, I made a discovery and thereby came in contact with one of
the mysteries of soil and plant life. We had stuck our pitchforks into
a haycock and had sprawled our long lean bodies in the small circular
shade made by our latest work of geoponic art. Fred stretched out his
right leg so he could reach into his hip pocket for his pocketknife,
with which he proceeded in a well-practiced manner to trim his finger-
nails. I observed this primitive manicure with some amusement as
with each deliberate, deft carving perfect half-moons dropped to the
ground.

My arm became sore with leaning on the sharp stubble, and I raised
myself into a sitting position. Aimlessly, I pulled one of the roots of

the soybean plant. The dirt around its roots was dry and it fell away, revealing a mass of things that resembled tiny eggs.

"What are these?" I asked my friend, curiously.

"Those are called nodules, Mel," Fred answered, returning the knife to his pocket, and pulling one of the roots at his side. "They contain nitrogen which the legume takes from the air and puts into the soil. That is why the soybean, especially when it is plowed under as green manure, becomes an excellent soil builder."

One year when my neighbor had surveyed his bean field, its foliage and pods of the Illini variety had grown so rank and full that in many places they had gone down. He had declared that there would be more hay than they would need. "I guess," he had said, "there'll be enough even for your old Cutie."

Just after we had shocked about twenty acres of soybeans, the rains came. It rained persistently day and night for about two weeks. All the beans molded so badly they had to be burned. It was not the thought of the many days of back-breaking, meticulous labor that made it so hard to set fire to the cocks of moldy hay, but rather the realization that there would be no hay now for my pet cow.

My memory is particularly good about the manner of shocking corn. I worked as hard as I could to keep up with Fred, who was a few years older than I, and to place the bundles just as he did. At first he would reset almost every one I stood up; sometimes he put one in a slightly different pocket in the shock; again he would place them just a little straighter than I had them. I learned to appreciate this extreme carefulness, however, after the shock rows were tied and the winds and rains came. Shocks in the neighboring fields would be lying flat on the ground and the leaves muddy and spoiled, while the shocks we had put up were straight and the leaves inside the shocks were sweet and green. It is not an easy matter to shock corn fodder so it will remain standing through the winter. Sometimes the wind was so strong while we were shocking that one of us had to hold the first bundles in place while the other built around them. Just as soon as the shock was finished, it was tied. There was an occasional shock that mushroomed out of shape despite all our efforts, however, especially where the corn was tall and broken down so badly that the bundles themselves were awkward and unbalanced.

There is always a great deal of manure to haul out onto the fields every spring; especially is this true on a dairy farm where the cows have been confined for so many months. There was an old cowshed on the Schlichting farm in which the young stock could shelter. The shed was cleaned out once a year, and the manure was so deep and packed that it was a gut-wrenching job to pull it apart with a fork and load it on the spreader. On one of these occasions I was helping Fred and his father. It was quite late in the spring — early May to be exact — before the more urgent work of preparing and planting the fields was done, and there was time to clean up the manure around the barnyard. The sun was unusually warm on this morning and by eleven o'clock was streaming in the east door of the shed, increasing the oppressive stench of the ammonia fumes as they escaped from the manure that we were pulling apart. The three of us worked silently most of the time, as the perspiration came out on our foreheads in tiny beads and soaked through the blue chambray shirts we were wearing.

Mr. Schlichting worked along with us, keeping up despite being many years our senior. His energies were tireless. He could walk for miles across the rough fields and boggy pastures and be in better wind at the end of the jaunt than most younger men.

There were times when I should have felt like taking a breathing spell and I suspected that Fred felt the same, but so long as Henry Schlichting kept working, we were obliged to keep going to save face. Not, however, until the spreader was loaded did Mr. Schlichting put down his fork. Then he walked over to the beater and began to cut twine strings that had become wrapped around it. An inquisitive heifer walked up to the spreader and sniffed it suspiciously, then jumped back in fright. I began with my bare hands to help him dislodge the twisted strings.

"Hey, Mel, ain't you got a knife?" Henry asked.

"No, sir," I replied, grinning sheepishly, "I ain't. I had one, but I lost it. I can't seem to keep a knife. They always fall out of my pocket somehow."

I was conscious that Fred, leaning his tall figure on the five-tined fork handle, was looking on, amusement on his square face. It nettled me a little to find him deriving so much delight at my embarrassment, and I stared at him with assumed displeasure. He only grinned the more, as he untied the red bandana from around his neck and wiped his brow with it.

Mr. Schlichting had removed his straw hat and had placed it on the wheel of the spreader while he was working at the beater. Another heifer now boldly approached, grabbed the hat, and pulled it from the wheel, letting it fall on the ground. The owner of the hat, upon discovering the plight of his headgear, turned and picked it up, shouting, "Dad-blast that critter!" The heifer kicked up her heels and was off in a cloud of dust.

Mr. Schlichting shook the dirt out of the straw hat and slammed it down over his white hair, then, turning to me, he gave me the knife in his hand. "Take it, and see that you don't lose it. No farmer goes without a pocketknife." Then, removing his Elgin watch from the bib pocket of his patched and faded overalls, he remarked, "Time to knock off for dinner."

I learned all the fundamentals of dairying from Mr. Schlichting and his son; the experience of many years has proved their methods infallible. They had very definite ideas on the building of a good dairy herd.

"Remember, Mel," Henry Schlichting told me one afternoon later in the summer while we were spading out Canadian thistles in his pasture, "great dairy cows are found in small herds as well as in the great herds of the country. In fact, many of the greatest cows of the breed were discovered in small farmer herds. Old Mother Pearl herself, the greatest brood cow of the breed, and the old Popeye cow that made the Dunloggin herd famous were only two of the great cows picked out of the sticks."

"I'll bet there aren't many cows as good as my Cutie," I said, jabbing the spade into the hard sod and prying up the long roots of the weed that is so difficult to kill.

"Your old Cutie is quite a cow, if I do have to say so," my friend smiled. "The pity is she's only a grade. You see you can never sell her offspring for good money because you can't register them. You don't know how she'll transmit either."

Shep, the dog, had been sleeping in the grass with one eye open. All at once the dog saw a gopher running through the grass and took after it, barking savagely.

"Are your cows as good as the cows we read so much about in the dairy magazines?" I asked, eager to continue the conversation with the experienced dairyman.

"Maybe they are and maybe they aren't," he replied noncommittally. "Advertising and ballyhoo may make a herd popular, but only wise breeding and culling will build a herd that'll keep the farmer-

breeder in the business. Many dairymen have been ruined by jumping
on the bandwagon and buying into a strain that was popular for the
moment. Find yourself a proved family of cows and stick to it, Mel."

I saw that the gopher had found his hole and had disappeared into
the ground, while Shep was barking disappointedly and digging the
dirt around the hole with determined fury. My attention was centered
more on Henry's words. He continued: "The truly great herd is built
around a particular cow family or families that have proved themselves after generations to be pure for high test, production, and
pleasing type. The fact that a cow makes a great record doesn't mean
she's a good cow to build a herd with. But if her daughters inherit
that ability then you want to keep that cow. By line-breeding to her
you are fairly sure that your future herd'll be as good as or better
than your present one. There'll always be a poor animal once in
a while no matter how careful you are in your breeding program.
Don't be afraid to send these to the butchers. Never sell such animals
as breeding stock."

"I know what line breeding is," I interrupted, "but how long can
one keep breeding to the same family? Won't there be a time when
new blood will have to be brought into the herd?"

"By being careful not to breed too closely to animals with known
weaknesses, and by culling out the poor ones, you can stick to such a
program a long time," my friend explained, uprooting the last thistle
in the patch we were working. "In time, yes, our herd may become
weak in one or more places and we'll have to bring in some outside
blood to strengthen our weak points. After this has been done,
though, we can go on with our," and my friend hesitated for the right
word, "original breeding program for a long time. The trouble some
of the big herds have with disease, constitutional weaknesses, and shy
breeding can be blamed onto prolonged close breeding without
culling."

Mr. Schlichting found a small flat board and began scraping the
dirt from his spade. I found a similar object along the creek bank and
proceeded to clean my tool. "That should be the last of the thistles
for now. A person has to keep them from going to seed or the farm'll
be overrun with them," Henry remarked, as we started toward home.
The sun was sinking red in the west as we followed the creek bank
through the pasture. I hazarded the opinion that according to the
old saying we would be in for a good day tomorrow. Shep had left

the gopher hole when he saw us leaving, and followed at our heels whimpering, with his tail between his legs.

I wanted to know more about breeding dairy cows, so I said, "There's a lot of talk nowadays about show type in our purebred animals. Is that more important than production?"

My neighbor turned his shrewd gray eyes on me and replied, "The most important thing to remember in breeding a dairy herd is this, Mel, and never forget it: Important as type is, a dairy cow is worth only market price if she can't produce. Dairy farmers make their living from the milk a cow gives, not from her looks. The reason, I believe, that the farmer-breeder more often has a higher producing herd than the large herds owned by the wealthy man who keeps cows for a hobby is because he culls his cows more severely. The farmer could not survive long if he did not adhere to this policy."

"Does the farmer, then, with his small herd of cows make the greatest contribution to the breed?" I asked.

"Not exactly," my friend answered amiably. "Men with the means can and should do what us poor farmers can't hope to do: Bring together these superior animals wherever they are to be found and mate them wisely. By doing this they can be a powerful means of improving our wonderful breed."

"Do you believe, then, that cows are the most important thing in the success of a dairy herd?" I asked, giving a pocket-gopher mound a vicious kick with my right foot.

"I didn't say that," he corrected, changing the spade into his other hand. "Good cows are most important; but the basis of all dairying is good quality hay and abundant pastures, and without them there can be no success with dairy cows."

On the Schlichting farm I had learned the meaning of those words "good quality hay and abundant pastures," which so many dairymen do not fully understand and appreciate. In spring the cows on my neighbor's farm grazed on rich blue grass pasture, a permanent pasture made untillable by a creek cutting through it. Then when the hot July sun withered the blue grass, the cows were turned into knee-deep Sudan grass. Sometimes they fed on a mixed legume meadow where they had to wade through red clover, timothy, and brome grass. In winter, they had bright green leafy alfalfa hay — all they could eat. It had a sweet smell. The cows loved it, and milked well all seasons of the year.

I was growing more curious all the time and asked my friend if good cows and good feed were the two most important factors in the successful operation of a dairy farm.

He shook his head, "There's still another thing to consider. In many ways it is the most important one of the three. If it's lacking, the whole operation is doomed to failure."

"What is it?" I asked inquisitively.

"The dairyman himself," was his answer. "The man who loves his cows doesn't think his work is drudgery, and the cow knows her master, and will respond to his attentions by increased milk flow. You'll learn, Mel, that if you love a cow, she'll know it, and will produce more milk for you than she will for any other person who takes care of her."

Now we passed through the gate and into the lane that led up to the yard by the big barn, and all at once the sun was out of sight behind the grove of willows and evergreens. The cows were waiting at the barn to be let in and to be milked.

In September I began my senior year in high school. For that reason I did not have much time to spend with the livestock or with the farm work. On Saturdays, however, I forgot everything but the forty and the cows. The grass in the pasture was now short and parched; fodder was cut every day and tossed across the fence to the cows. I loved this chore because I enjoyed watching the animals work over the stalks, hunting for the bright yellow ears of corn. Cows love corn better than anything else. They learn to stand by the fence, waiting for their master to toss the fodder to them, with heads high and eyes turned wistfully toward the cornfield, listening sharply as the breezes rustle the dry leaves in the field.

One day while the cattle fed boisterously on the fodder, I sat under the shade of a nearby oak tree, watching them with interest and amusement. My thoughts drifted away from them after a while; then I thought regretfully of the following spring when my schooldays would be ended, and I should have to face life with all its deepest realities. As yet I had made no plans for the future. But I had spent hour after hour under the old tree in the pasture, dreaming of the forty in the years to come. A gnawing, indefinable ambition began to grow within me. I had lived and worked with those noble dairy cows for two years now, and I fancied I saw the herd that would come from them. Then I realized the seed of this grand idea had become imbedded in the fertile soil of my mind, and must wait for the years to give it its growth.

The winter passed imperceptibly as all winters pass on an Iowa farm. There were the regular chores to do each day, wood-cutting in the willow grove along the west line fence, the pump to be thawed out on cold mornings, snow to be shoveled around the yards, fodder to be chopped out of the shock and hauled to the barn, and the hen-house to be cleaned.

By spring Cutie was well along in her lactation period, and was still milking exceptionally well. Cutie always insisted upon occupying the first stall in the barn so she could be the first to be fed; then, too, she might turn her curious eyes out the door whenever it chanced to be open. I found time in the evenings after school to curry and brush her until her hair shone like black velvet and priceless ermine. The tail switch was scrubbed and combed out until it was as soft and white as the down in a ripened milkweed pod. Indeed, Cutie was already an animal to be proud of.

In April, Billie was sold. This was a sad event on the farm. Even Oliver, whose only interest in the herd had been his own cow, shed tears when the young bull was loaded into the truck. Billie, with his docility and antics, had become a favorite with all of us. To make a tender scene more touching, Cutie came bellowing up to the truck, poked her wet nose through the truck slats, and rubbed it against her youngster's face in a last affectionate bovine kiss. As the truck drove out of the yard, I put my arm around Cutie's neck to let her know that I was sorry for her, and said, "Your nose is running, Cutie. Better use your hanky."

Then with the long tongue with which nature had wonderfully equipped her, she slipped it deftly and handsomely in the curve of her nostril, wiping away the saliva from her muzzle.

There was a noticeable change in Cutie now that she was no longer a heifer. The earlier playfulness she had always exhibited had mellowed into a patient, less wayward disposition; although there were still times when, as my father used to say, "you couldn't trust that critter!" Cutie was larger, deeper-bodied, and more splendidly marked than ever. The fetus was well along in its formation, and the hope that my wonderful cow would drop a heifer calf was again revived. By May, Cutie, in preparation for the great event, was seldom if ever seen with the other members of the herd.

It was in May, too, that I was graduated from high school. I was excited for weeks before graduation day, not only because an important phase of my life was ending and a greater one about to begin, but also for the reason that I had been privileged to deliver the valedictory on commencement day. When the special night arrived, I was so nervous when I faced the crowd of people that it is hard for me to remember anything that happened. I remember I faltered dreadfully, but some of the words ring back to me now with an eloquence they never carried when they were uttered so many years ago:

"Dear parents, teachers, and friends . . . this quiet haven . . . appreciation and thoughtfulness . . . our teachers . . . wise piloting . . . your precepts . . . unknown waters . . . a greater journey . . . face every hazard bravely . . . sail to success. . . ."

The salutatorian of the class was also a boy, Andy Roeder, who rendered his address like the true orator that he was. There were the diplomas awarded by the president of the school board, the warm hand claspings and words of praise and encouragement from friends and relatives — and it was over. How the courage and hope we felt that night might have failed us had we been able to see what lay ahead! Happily, we had no way then of knowing that in a few short years the second World War would claim for its first casualty in our own home town the salutatorian of my class; that for many of us it would be the last time on this earth we would see each other's friendly faces; that shortly the fine old school building itself with all its records would be completely destroyed by fire; or that for me life itself would hold so many heartaches and triumphs.

The drive home late that night with my parents and Judy will always be a shadow across my memory. Already a dreadful sadness had come over me. I seemed to have lost something very real and dear to me — something precious that could never be recaptured. My father's voice awakened me from this stupor.

"Well, Melvin, now that you have graduated, what do you intend to do?"

I was surprised at this question. I had never thought of being anything else but a dairy farmer, and I had believed my father knew this.

"I want to stay on the farm," I said falteringly.

He chuckled, not unkindly. "Son, there isn't any future in farming the way prices are going now. Anyway, farming is for those who haven't enough brains to do anything else. For those like myself who have had no high school education. With your brother's help I can manage the farm. Besides, you are not strong enough to be a farmer, and with your talents, you might get somewhere in this world."

"But, Father," I protested, "I don't care for any other kind of work. And you are wrong about farming's being for the uneducated. Farming requires the best education we can obtain. It is because farmers as a whole are not better educated that they have not been able to unite like the men in other trades for better prices and better standards of living. If farmers could only realize the tremendous task and responsibility that is theirs, they would practice better farming methods and save the land; for when the soil is lost, the welfare of the nation is lost."

"Idle talk, son," my mother interrupted. "Your health compels you to choose some easier, less strenuous occupation."

"Have you ever thought of teaching school?" my father suggested.

No, I certainly had not.

"Well, Melvin, there's no hurry," my father concluded the discussion as we turned into the gateway at the farm. "There'll be plenty of time later to decide, and I know you'll change your mind about farming. Perhaps next year you and Judy both will want to take a normal training course and find yourselves schools."

I was sure I should never change my mind about the farm, nor should I ever be happy away from it. Strange how it gets into one's blood, and nothing can get it out. I had tried to fight it at first. Once I had looked upon farming as sordid and degrading; but something, perhaps the little heifer, had changed all of that, and I had surrendered. I could fight against it no longer.

III

Drought and Blizzard

THERE had been little snow during the winter of 1934, and less rain the following spring; as a result, by early June when the pastures should have been lush and green they were instead becoming crisp and brown. In May, Cutie had already dried up in answer to the primal law, in order that her body might be rebuilt in preparation for another lactation. Her hips were rounding out with fat, and her entire body was growing sleek and plump. She was the only cow in the herd that usually freshened in midsummer.

It became necessary now to herd the cows along the roadside where the forage was still green though quite rank. Those were pleasant, carefree hours I spent every morning herding those four noble creatures. While the cows grazed contentedly, I sprawled beneath a shade tree along the fence and became absorbed in one of Scott's thrilling tales. Sometimes I just sat and looked across the landscape as far as my eyes could see, and when my gaze, like the earth, became lost in the interminable sky beyond, I was conscious only of breathing the sheer joy of living. There was always about me the sweet song of the robin; the deep, rich trilling notes of the friendly meadow lark perched on a nearby fence post; and the strident piping of an old pheasant cock as he resumed once more his carefree bachelor days. A honeybee would buzz dangerously close by me and stop to guzzle the nectar from a golden dandelion. Perhaps by now the cows had wandered too far down the road, and I must turn them around before they reached the neighbor's cornfield gate; the cows knew full well the gate would be open, that if they munched grass nonchalantly until they could catch me off guard they could make a beeline for the opening, and then they would see how I could get them out. Once more ahead of them, I could pause to hunt the patches of wild strawberry, the immaculate faces of their flowers peeping out of the grass under my feet; and I would stoop in search of the crimson, luscious fruit.

As the hours went lazily by, my gluttonous charges became round and full as apple barrels in the fall, and made for a shady spot to rest and regurgitate their breakfast. The sun was riding high in the heavens, and the earth radiating warmth. All this told me it was time to take the cows back home for water. They were thirsty when they reached the water tank, and drank long, refreshing draughts. The rest of the day they would spend in the east alfalfa meadow.

One morning it was particularly hot and sultry. There was no dew on the grass when I took the cows out on the road for their usual morning feed. The excessive heat of the morning wearied the animals long before their appetites were satisfied. I, therefore, turned them into the alfalfa field sooner than was their custom and left them for the day.

Shortly after dinner a cloud appeared in the southwest. Soon the whole sky was overcast, and a brisk wind started blowing. The black clouds billowed across the sky. Suddenly the heavens were rent by lightning and the earth trembled with the rumbling of thunder; then it appeared the bottom of the sky might be falling out as a torrent of rain deluged the porous fields and meadows.

I had been plowing the west piece of corn with the old one-row horse cultivator, and was caught in the rain. By the time I reached the yard and drove the team between the cribs I was soaked.

Then, as if in derision, the rain stopped pouring and the sun came out all at once brilliant and warm, painting an endless rainbow in the east. The opening in the sky closed as suddenly as it had appeared and remained sealed the entire period of that long, terrible summer.

I was drying myself by the kitchen fire when I first heard it — the sound I could distinguish from a thousand others, the soft, calf-like lowing of Cutie; only now it was louder, more pleading. It was the sound of an animal in great distress.

I rushed from the house without putting on my boots and saw Cutie walking back and forth along the fence, bellowing to attract attention. And then I saw it all in one horrified glance. Her left side was raised high over her back, and she looked like an inflated balloon. Two of the cows were already rolling and moaning on the ground, while Pet was backing up, swaying from one side to the other, trying to lie down but not succeeding. They were bloated!

This was my first experience of the kind. I was, nevertheless, fully aware of the danger the cows were in. Without wasting any time I dashed frantically to my neighbors. I found both Mr. Schlichting and Fred in the machine shed changing shovels on their new tractor cultivator.

"What's the trouble now, Mel?" the older man asked.

"The cows are bloated!" I gasped breathlessly.

"Where are they?"

"Out in the yard. They're bloated bad."

"Come on, Fritz, we'll go down and see what we can do for them."

Fred helped me get the animals stanchioned in the barn. They were really in great distress by this time. Mr. Schlichting had been cutting pieces from an old broom handle and had tied small ropes to each stick in the manner of bridles. In no time at all each cow had a stick in her mouth and was chewing away vigorously, the idea being that as the cows chewed, the gas was belched up.

Cutie must have realized we were trying to help her, for she accepted the bit in her mouth without resentment and commenced chewing away as though the broom handle were the most palatable of dainties. The other cows, somewhat skeptical, were more reluctant in taking to the bits; hence, by the time they were masticating, Cutie's sides had shrunk to their normal size.

In late June, Cutie calved, and true to her old tricks disappointed me again by dropping a bull calf. I would have upbraided my pet for being so persistent in bringing bulls into a world where they were not wanted, but I loved her too much for that. She was in excellent condition, and her milk flow was so great after this freshening that it became necessary to milk her three times every day. So strong was her desire to be milked that she followed me around whenever I carried a pail. At this time there was no such thing as ground feed on our farm for the dairy cows. When we were fortunate enough to have ear corn or whole oats I did raid the bins for special meals for my pet; but then only when my father did not know it. He did not believe in wasting valuable grain on a milk cow that "should live on the grass of the earth." Cutie was producing from fifteen to twenty quarts of milk three times a day that summer despite all the adverse conditions of those times. I had grown to love her from the day when my father had first given her to me, but it was only now for the first time that I realized I owned one of the best dairy cows in the state.

Cutie was eating all the time, and never seemed to get filled up. When I let her out of the pasture to obtain additional forage on the road and in the house yard, my father scolded me severely.

"Cutie is no better than the other cows," he would say. "Put her back in the pasture."

"But, Dad, she gives more milk than they do," I argued. "She just has to have more to eat than they do. There isn't anything to eat in the pasture any more. Let her eat a little while on the road. She'll turn around by herself when she gets so far and come home."

"Put her back in the pasture!" my father said with finality.

There was an old apple tree growing in the pasture that usually had a few apples on it. Cutie used to watch them high above her reach, and after a time she would stretch her long neck as far as she could and grab hold of a branch with apples on it. After she had pulled the limb down so that the apples were within her reach, she discovered that if she let go the bough the fruit would swing back again out of her reach. She would reach for them again, and while she was figuring a way to get the apples, the other three cows would come and eat them all.

HENRY SCHLICHTING FARM — ARNEWOOD PASTURE IN FOREGROUND

THE HENRY SCHLICHTING FAMILY
Edna, Meta, Lydia, Fred, and Henry S.

CUTIE

CUTIE AND HER BULL CALF

When I found her in this predicament, I climbed the tree and shook the apples to the ground. Cutie gulped them down as fast as they fell from the tree. Mother caught us in this act several times, and mildly reproved.

"Son, would you rather let Cutie eat the few apples we have, or eat them yourself in a pie?"

"I'd rather let Cutie have them."

Mother would walk away muttering good-humoredly to herself, "What can you do with a boy like that?"

I was as happy then as any boy could be. Everything seemed so sweet on this earth. The farm I had had no choice but to accept became the dearest home I had ever known. How many times since the curtain has fallen over this great act in the play of life have nostalgic memories turned back to that little farm and to the black and white cow that made it what it was; how many times have I wakened from poignant dreams of that place so real to me still. How many times I cannot count!

I was happier than I had any right to be. I was not at all prepared for the second shattering blow that was to come into my life. In a frantic effort to "keep going" my father sold first the machinery that he had used on the road, then the livestock. Not until the milch cows began to leave did I become worried. When the last four were all that were left, I felt they at least would never be sold.

The summer came on and with it a drought unusual in Iowa. The pastures dried up, the corn withered and turned brown before the ears could form, and the entire countryside that had always been so fruitful lay barren and desolate. Day after day the sun beat down relentlessly. Wells so vital for supplying water to the thirsty livestock went dry one by one. The papers carried frightful tales of the Dakotas: of swine and cattle starving to death; of dust, that insidious terror of the middle border; and of entire regions laid waste by the lack of rain. Truck load after truck load of half-starved cattle and hogs from these drought-stricken states arrived in Iowa and states to the south and east to be sold at "give away" prices. Hot, parching winds whipped incessantly over the crisp earth, picking up the barren soil in black clouds and piling it in huge drifts in the road ditches and along fence rows. Day after day the hot winds blew the loose dirt so that one could not see the house from the barn. Dirt and dust and weed seed blew into Iowa from as far away as the Dakotas. And al-

ways when the wind did not blow, the sun continued to throw its
torrid rays over an arid, dying countryside.

And then came winter, worse by far than the summer had been, a
nightmare to farmers everywhere. Feed could not be bought even if
one had the money with which to pay for it. Yet the stock had to
live. The cornstalks in the fields had been short and were covered
deeply with snow, so it became almost impossible for cattle to find
any feed from this source. Any kind of feed at all sold for exorbitant
prices. Earlier in the winter my father had managed to buy a few
tons of foxtail hay at $20 per ton for our four cows. Some farmers
cut down their trees one by one for the cattle to munch on the meager
diet of leaves and bark. To make this dire situation worse, the cold
weather and unceasing blizzards and snow made that winter of 1935
unprecedented for scores of years in Iowa.

Our hearth did not know the luxury of coal to keep the family
around it warm and comfortable; green, sputtering, hand-sawed
clumps of wood aided by dry cobs from the crib made a modicum of
warmth. On the coldest nights my father and mother took turns
beside the fire, keeping wood on it, so we would not get cold in bed.

One of these nights I shall never forget. It was on a Saturday. The
snow had been blowing out of the northwest all during the day with
such an intensity that it had been impossible for a person to see anything in front of him but the impenetrable white cloud of driving
snow. Earlier in the afternoon my father and Oliver had taken Prince,
the blind horse, to the stubble-field to haul in the last shocks of fodder. My father had to chop the outside bundles loose with a grub hoe
while Oliver held Prince by the bridle to keep him from walking
away. A chain was fastened around the shock and then hooked into
a clevis that was attached to the singletree. My father then grabbed
Prince's bridle and coaxed the horse to go ahead. Only in this way
was it possible to get the animal to face the razor-sharp snow. Heav-
ing, lurching, stumbling through the great drifts, Prince succeeded
in pulling the shock free and bringing it up close to the stable door.

By this time I had the cows milked and fed, and after putting the
horse away for the night, we hurried to the house. After supper the
dishes were cleared from the table and we huddled around it to play
five hundred. All through the day my mother had anxiously expressed
the hope that the wind would die down when the sun set, but instead
with the coming of night the blizzard gained in momentum, the

temperature dropped to 29 degrees below zero, and the cold pene-
trated easily through the weathered siding of the old frame house.

During weather like this we practically lived in the dining room.
The kitchen floor was so cold that Mother could not stand on it without wearing her overshoes. After the meals were cooked on the range,
the kitchen was shut off. The rooms on the west were never used at
all during the winter. They served merely as storerooms for all of
the furniture we had had in the big town house.

The Round Oak stove, its iron belly red hot, stood in the living
room. On top of it the teakettle was steaming cheerfully, while huddled beside the kettle were Mother's flatirons that she would later
wrap in flannel and take to bed with her. Crowded as we were in the
single room, there was one item Mother had insisted on keeping in it.
That was her fernery with its many beautifully-leafed ferns and
special geraniums. On the really cold nights such as this one she would
have the fernery pulled away from the window and would place newspapers on the window side of her plants to keep them from freezing,
for despite the terrific heat from the stove that would cause one's face
to become flushed near it, water on the floor in the corners of the
room would be freezing.

"Indicate in spades," I said, rather indifferently, after spreading my
cards out in my hand. Then, after looking at Oliver's beaming face,
I decided I might as well have passed the bid.

"Nine hearts!" he shouted, rising out of his chair.

"I guess they have all the cards this time," Judy, my partner, said
despairingly. "I pass."

"Take it," my father said, and shoved the blind to my brother, who
grabbed it up eagerly.

"Get anything in the blind?" I asked Oliver.

"Just one little heart and an ace."

"They must have all the trumps between them," Judy concluded.
She placed her "hand" face down on the table, and began applying
finger nail polish to her nails while she was waiting for Oliver to re-
arrange his cards.

"Did you put the oilcloth over the tablecloth before you started
your game?" Mother asked solicitously, the thought just coming to
her, and looked up from her quilting, the needle suspended in mid-
air, to find that her fears were unnecessary.

The game continued and the evening wore on. Roselyn and Eldena were quietly doing some homework, using the sewing machine as a stand for their books, with only an occasional exchange of words between them. Once I glanced at Mother in her rocking chair with the pretty flower garden quilt spread on her lap. Her face, always serene and lovely, was pale and drawn with just a shade of color caused by the heat from the stove. There were a few streaks of gray in her reddish-brown hair that had always been heavy and naturally wavy. She had not been well since moving to the farm, and she was no longer so active as she had been.

The telephone rang just once during the evening; the call had been on the line to one of the neighbors. Judy jumped up from the table to "rubber in" on the conversation. This was one diversion practically all rural folks indulged in, especially in the winter when there was not much else to do.

"Lydia talking to Mrs. Benn," Judy commented, her hand over the mouthpiece.

"I'll bet they're talking about the men," Eldena speculated, forgetting her studies momentarily.

"They're cussing them up and down," Judy affirmed. "Because of the blizzard they've been under their feet all day in the house."

"Aw, quit rubbering and play cards!" Oliver complained loudly. "It's your turn to play."

Judy replaced the receiver and rejoined us at the table, saying sarcastically, "You're just growly because you've been losing all night."

"Well," Oliver replied, mildly reproachful, "I haven't been getting much cooperation from my partner."

My father laid down his cards wearily, his brow knit as if something were troubling him. "Ain't got my mind on cards tonight," he said, with a long sigh; then abruptly turned his chair away from the table, and blurted out what had been on his mind all evening, "Confound it, Jo, we're going to have to sell the milch cows!"

The room was suddenly still as death. It seemed to me then that even the storm outside had heard and had been quelled by the greater impact of my father's words. At least to me the blizzard was silent, but the deafening ringing in my mind was unbearable.

My mother dropped her hands in her lap, and the color drained from her face. "What do you mean, Art? We can't sell the cows!"

"Either sell them or let them starve," he said bitterly, and added, "and us, too. There is very little feed left for them."

"All of them?" I asked, my voice choking with emotion. "Not — Cutie!"

"Do you want her to die?" he returned almost angrily, but his eyes were turned from me.

"She won't die!" I cried, trembling with fear, anguish, and reproach. "I'll see that she has enough to eat. Don't sell *her*!"

"Let him keep her," Mother said, pleading my cause. "We've got to have milk for the house."

"I suppose you think I am a beast," my father said remorsefully. "I don't like this either. But all right, keep her; but if she don't live through the winter, don't blame me!"

It was several days before the snowplow opened the road to town so that a truck could get through to load the cows. Strange that such a tragic scene as the one that took Twinkletoes, Pet, and Blackie away from me forever should bring with it a feeling of relief — relief that Cutie would be left behind alone.

Poor Cutie did poorly on the feed left for her, withered cornstalks without any ears on them and a little musty straw. There was no grain or hay of any kind. Perhaps it was as well there was no feed to buy, for we had no means to buy it with. There was scarcely more to eat in the house.

I tried my best to make my cow as comfortable as I could that long, bleak winter, and I am sure my efforts saved her from dying. Her last calf had died, and Cutie still had no heifer calf to carry on her greatness. The barn was poor enough with all the cattle in it; it was bitterly cold after the herd had been sold. The windows were broken out and I boarded them shut the best I knew how. The stable had consisted of twelve wooden stanchions too close together, a dirt floor lower than the outside so that every spring when the rains came there would be a foot or two of water across the stable floor, and the cows had to stay outdoors. I can remember how cold and numb my fingers got milking the cows on those frosty mornings. I had dreamed of the time when there would be a cement floor in the barn with a gutter and steel stanchions in place of the old wooden ones, so the cows would not have sore briskets and legs any more.

These improvements seemed very remote that winter. I made my cow a stall in the warmest corner of the barn, and kept it as dry as I could with the little bedding we had. For special treats I would bring her an apple, a beet, or a potato. How well I knew she loved these dainties. Every fall when we were digging our potatoes with the old mare pulling the walking plow, Cutie followed the rows and gulped the vegetables faster than we could pick them up. She did appreciate these small favors that cold winter. After chewing each treat with lingering pleasure, she would rub her soft head against me, look at me with those sad, wide-open eyes of hers, and lick my face and hands with her rough tongue; then, if another apple or beet were not forthcoming, she would give me a gentle butt.

The barn was sometimes so cold that I'd have to stop milking and warm my hands under Cutie's flanks. Mornings when it was 20 and 30 degrees below zero, I came into the barn to find Cutie with hoary icicles hanging from her muzzle. I carried water for her from the pump through great drifts of snow. Several mornings my father had to thaw out the pump before we could get water; the bitter, north wind cut down upon us, unchecked by lack of a windbreak. The marrow-freezing cold sapped all my energy, left the world white and dead. Nature was not always so gentle as I had believed it to be.

It was almost unbelievable that the world could ever be rid of all the snow the winter had left, that it could ever be warmed again. But the vernal season came at last, as it has done ever since the world began; and the hideous terrors of the winter were forgotten in the great blessings of a reassuring spring.

IV

Teaching School

I HAD BEEN completely happy and satisfied on the farm. Deep inside I had resolved to become a good herdsman and develop one of the finest herds in the county; but once more circumstances worked against me. Gradually there had come a shadow across the sweet bliss of life on the farm. That shadow was my father. He was a man of great determination and strong purpose. I am indebted to him for the same traits of character. I suppose it was only natural that two minds so much alike should be continually clashing. When he had the means, my father was one of the greatest philanthropists I have known. But his closest friends upon whom he had lavished all sorts of generosities deserted him when his money was gone. He tried to drown his troubles in drink, and during those times his family suffered greatly. Then I saw in my own home the sordidness and terrible effects that drinking had caused to several families I knew well, and I grew to despise the curse with all the hate that was in me.

Matters did not improve. On one occasion when we quarreled, I told him with all the pent-up bitterness that was in me that I hated him. My father's words to me will always ring in my mind, hurting me, rebuking me, "Melvin, I think the world of you, but you won't forgive me for something I cannot help."

There was not enough work on the farm for all of us, and the only solution for me seemed to be to leave. I was miserable. Judy and I decided to get schools and start teaching. In January we took our teacher's examinations in Mason City and, having passed them, began our search for schools. In those days there were a hundred teachers after the same school. This I say without being guilty of hyperbole. One cannot realize the difficulty a beginning teacher experienced in getting a school. We were fortunate after much effort to obtain schools two miles apart.

One beautiful day in June, 1936, Judy and I had our suitcases packed, ready to attend the normal training course at Iowa State Teachers College in Cedar Falls. As children, my sister and I had been inseparable. I would not even practice the violin unless Judy accompanied me on the piano. Without the piano I was lost. Alone, the notes of the violin became harsh and discordant; I would lose all sense of tempo. Together we played very well.

I looked in my suitcase just before we were ready to leave to make sure that I had my favorite picture of Cutie with me. I had milked her as usual that morning, and tried not to think of leaving her for three long months. I decided I would not see her before I left. With that plan in mind, I thought I could get away without creating a scene.

But everything did not go off so smoothly. Cutie was eating grass by the gate as we drove out of the yard, and when I got out of the car to open the gate, she stopped eating and walked toward me. I was never so wretched in all my life. Leaving her behind was like losing everything I ever loved. Only one who has owned such an animal can understand how I felt that morning in June when even nature seemed to chide me with her splendor. My pet licked my hands with her long, rough tongue as though she realized I was going away. I threw my arms around her neck as the tears rolled bitterly, unrestrainedly down my cheeks.

Cedar Falls is a beautiful place in summer. Its trees are magnificent, its homes luxurious. The campus is located about a mile from the city proper on College Hill. It is enclosed by a low brick wall, broken by several entrances that lead to the college's many fine buildings, which are grouped around an inner and outer square.

Judy roomed at Bartlett Hall, the women's dormitory; I had a room in the beautiful, modern Baker Hall that had only recently been completed and was opened for the first time. Just outside my window was the Campanile, erected in 1926 as a memorial to the founders and builders of the college. The imposing shaft of the Campanile, which rises 100 feet, is one of the foremost monuments in Iowa; it is topped with a belfry, Italian Renaissance in style, in which a fifteen-bell set of chimes is played at regular intervals during the day. Another feature of this monument is the world's prize-winning Fasoldt Clock which stands on the second floor and sounds Westminster Chimes every fifteen minutes.

At first I was lonely, but as the days and weeks passed I was swept along by the spirit of campus life. I made new acquaintances, I had classes to attend (these were for the most part in the form of lectures), spent many hours in the library, and during my leisure time I indulged in movies, sports, forums, and "sings." Two very popular songs heard at the "sings" during the summer were *Slumber Boat* and *Beautiful Dreamer*. Both songs thrilled me then and always will. Sometimes on Saturdays Judy and I took picnic lunches and walked into the country or visited one of the many lovely parks in this verdant city.

How we watched the mails for letters from home, and when either of us received one, we would read it over and over together. Our little sisters were twelve and fourteen years of age, and they wrote often. We laughed as we read their amusing letters. And Mother wrote to one of us every other day. In every letter from home there was always some mention of Cutie; I would skim through them until I came to the parts that told of my pet. They were always interesting for me. She was always getting into some mischief. One Sunday while everyone was away at church, Cutie ate all the flowers in Mother's window boxes. She was always drinking the water — dirty as it was — out of the troughs that watered the ducks and geese.

At last came a week end we could go home. It was almost sunset when we reached the forty. I ran to the pasture gate at once and called my cow by name. Cutie was on the other side of the hill, but when she heard her name, she came wading through the tall brown grass toward me. She licked my hands until they were sore. I fed her oats out of my hand from a bucket I had filled in the granary. I stroked her soft hair, and, as I talked to her, all the troubles in the world were gone. She rubbed her nose against me.

"You ain't even listening, Cutie," I scolded. "All you think of is your belly."

At last she lay down at my feet, and began chewing her cud. She was happy and content. I left her drowsing in the tepid starlight and walked to the house, promising myself I would see her bright and early in the morning.

Summer school was out the last of August, and I began teaching the first Monday in September. I was reminded many times during those first weeks of teaching of the advice given to me earlier by one of my former high school teachers. I had kept up a correspondence with her during those years when her profession took her from the large metropolis of New York to Anaconda, Montana, "among the dusty chinooks and icy blizzards of the Bitter Roots of the Rockies" and back again across our great United States to Chicago. In one of her letters, she had written: "Greedily drink in all you can as to school methods and management, but — next September don't be at all discouraged if you find it necessary to disregard everything and settle your own problems in your own way, in spite of Judd and Company. This frequently happens, for very often situations demand good old horse sense (or cow sense, if you prefer that brand)!"

At this crisis in my life, as well as at others, this favorite teacher of mine was ready with her kind words of praise and wisdom, her helpful criticisms and suggestions. How I wished that I could be as good a teacher as she was, that I could exact the same effort and attachment from my pupils that she received from me.

I worked long hours after school and on week ends, reviewing the lessons for the following week for the nine grades that I had to teach. Few persons know that it takes a rural teacher longer to plan his or her classes than it takes for the lessons to be recited. It was the first time I had ever been inside a country school, and very different it was from the small-town school where I had received my education. Nine different grades in one room! I had never heard of such a thing. Each class was called to the front of the room and sat on a bench in front of my desk. Most of the classes consisted of only one or two children, and lasted not more than fifteen minutes. It was easier for the children at their seats in the other grades to become interested in the class going on in the front of the room than it was to keep studying their own lessons at their seats.

I had three beginners in first grade and one little girl in kindergarten. They were taught to read by flash cards instead of phonics, which had been the accepted method of teaching beginners to read when I was a child. One of the little boys in first grade had been in the same grade for three years; it soon became apparent that as far as his being able to learn was concerned, he would have to stay in first grade until he was fifty unless a kindhearted teacher came along and passed him.

There were many times outside of school when I was called on for assistance. During the noon hour one day one of my first graders became fastened to a tree out on the playground when his pony got excited and ran around the tree to which it was tied. Another trying incident occurred when one of the boys (and he was a chubby one) swallowed an ink eraser and had to be suspended in mid-air by his legs until the eraser dropped out on the floor.

The visit to the school by the newly elected county superintendent of schools was an awesome event for both the pupils and for their teacher. The former superintendent was a kindly old lady, who paid her annual visit to the schools with a smile on her face and left with a few words like, "My, what nice children you are!" "What intelligent pupils you have!" or "Your schoolroom is decorated beautifully!"

Her successor, however, was her exact opposite. She was a woman of brilliant scholastic achievements. Her appearance was always serious, even stern. She was a personage who demanded respect and awe. She entered the room without knocking, sat in on the class in progress, and took notes as she scrupulously examined the pupils, room, and teacher. To my great embarrassment, my third grade boy, who was on the recitation bench and had been noticing for some time the eyes of the lady upon him, suddenly asked her: "Lady, are you mad at me?"

It was fortunate in many ways that Judy's school was just two miles from my own. We drove a Model T Ford coupe back and forth from home to school. Spelling bees as well as games of different kinds were engaged in between the two schools, and there came to be a friendly rivalry between them.

My incorrigible first grader was paying too much attention to my seventh grade hygiene class one day when I was explaining that milk was a food and as such should be chewed and not gulped down. The next day the boy's older sister came to me with this story.

"Mr. Scholl, my brother almost got his pants warmed last night."

"How was that, Beulah?" I asked.

"You remember telling the seventh grade yesterday they should chew their milk? Well, Junior was swishing his milk back and forth in his mouth last night at the supper table, his cheeks all blown out of shape, when daddy asked him what the devil he was doing. When he said he was chewing his milk, daddy was just ready to slap his face. But I explained that teacher told us to do that. He just looked at me."

At Christmas time we had a program at night and everyone was invited. I had had a great deal of trouble making my kindergarten girl recite the welcome recitation. She was a very sweet child, and we were all looking forward to her little part on the great night. Her mother bought her a new pink and blue dress especially for the program, and she looked like a live doll. But when the curtain was pulled, she stood in the front of the room with her finger in her mouth, swaying her tiny hips from side to side, and refusing to say a single word. I started prompting her. Her mother coaxed her. All to no avail. The rest of the program was concluded without further mishap.

The worst blizzard of the winter was on Washington's Birthday. It being a holiday, Judy and I were at home. True to the tradition of teachers getting to their schools, we took our suitcases and books and trudged over snowbanks six feet deep to get to our districts. For the rest of the winter we boarded near our schools, and for several weeks I did not see Cutie. During those terribly cold weeks I was tormented by the thought that she was lying in the cold barn without any straw, and with most of the windows out. I knew, too, that there was no hay in the barn and that she had to go out in the cornfield and pick at the dry stalks and leaves, mostly buried under deep snow. I tried to crowd the picture out of my mind. The water tank covered with a foot of ice with a hole broken in it the size of Cutie's mouth haunted me even while I was sleeping.

I was now boarding with my Uncle Dave and Aunt Jane. My uncle lived on a farm about two miles from my school; the place had been his home ever since I was a small boy. He had always been my favorite uncle, and it was one of the rare delights of my boyhood to visit at his farm.

At this time an important event occurred within our family circle. My two younger sisters were as different as they were inseparable. It had seemed only yesterday that they were babies. Judy, Oliver, and I started to school before the two youngest sisters were born; naturally enough when they arrived on the scene, they grew up together. Eldena was the baby of the family and Father's favorite. She had rosy cheeks, freckles, and flaming red hair that intensified her tempestuous, boyish disposition. My father put the boxing gloves on her when she was five; when she was nine years old, the twelve-year-old boys in the neighborhood knew better than to pick a fight with her. Roselyn, older and larger, was easily subdued by her younger sister. As a little girl she was fair and quiet, and, as everyone said, "a little angel."

It should not have been a surprise, then, when Roselyn suddenly told us, in her own quiet way, that she wanted to go to the convent. At first we were taken aback that a girl of fifteen could know what she wanted; yet we realized very soon that she was determined. My mother, always deeply religious, was very much pleased. My father was inwardly very much elated, but said to her, mostly to test her, "But supposing I won't let you go?"

I remember her ready answer, "Oh, I will go anyway."

And go she did. The years that followed attested her earlier convictions. Though she had several years in which to make up her mind whether or not she wished to stay in the convent, she remained steadfast in her decision. At the age of twenty-one, Roselyn took her final vows of poverty, chastity, and obedience in the Dominican Order of Sisters, and became known at the "Mound" as the "quiet little mouse of Sinsinawa." She took for her new name "Sister Mary Germaine."

Spring was just peeping out from under the blanket of winter. Grass, the greatest of all the farmer's crops, was growing without any expenditure of money or labor on his part; the crocus and the violet, the pussy willow and the anemone were splashing this green gold with vivid color. The school children felt this call of nature, and romped and played out-of-doors. The last little drifts of snow under the evergreen trees in the school yard and along the ditches beside the road where the snow had been deepest felt at last the warm rays of the sun and melted into tiny rivulets that meandered among last year's mat of brown grass and pine needles.

Then came the closing day of school. That day will always remain fresh and dear in my memory. To be with a group of children for nine months not only as a teacher, but as a friend, nurse, and what-have-you, and then to have to say farewell is a very touching and sad experience. There was a picnic out in the yard for the children and all the families in the district, with plenty to eat and with ice cream paid for out of funds raised from programs given during the school year. The children were happy with the anticipation of glorious vacation times ahead. Last of all, both parents and children came to their teacher expressing their sorrow that he was leaving them, thanking him for all he had done for them, and wishing for him the best of everything in the future. And these were the words of a small boy to remember:

"Mummy told me we wasn't t' have you next year. I want t' say g'bye cuz I'll never see you no more. I liked the stories you ollays told us 'bout the little birds that He put in the trees, 'n the an'mals that give us our food, 'n the ground that gives daddy a job. When I grow up, I want to be a farmer like my daddy."

The Death of Cutie

AFTER SCHOOL was out in May, I went back to the farm and Cutie. The farm had gone back to the loan company that had held the mortgage, and the only way we could continue living there was to rent it. My father no longer cared what happened to the place after that; he decided to go back on the road and finally got a job with a construction company that was building an overhead near Eldora. The nervous tension of the schoolroom had not been agreeable to my health; so I took over the farm myself.

I had read that the life of the struggling artist is very hard indeed; the song writer almost starves to death before his first song is accepted and his talents are recognized. But I was to learn for myself the difficulties that confront a farmer in building a fine herd of registered Holsteins. Those were bad times for the average farmer, and purebreds always cost more to get into than grades. I had a one-year lease on the farm. I had Cutie, and I had the very strongest desire to succeed. Even now I suppose that was enough to ask for.

Cutie had always had a calf every year, usually in early summer. I returned to the farm to discover that she was not with calf and it had been a year since she had last freshened. That was an appalling situation to begin with; yet my cow was still milking.

I had two good friends that stood me in good stead at this time. It was in early September, 1937, and I was helping Mr. Schlichting and Fred shock corn. I was hired for a dollar a day, which was the prevailing wage on the farm at that time. I always ate my dinner with them. After dinner I usually sat listening to the two men discussing Holsteins. I was not familiar then with the greatest families within the breed, but I was very much interested. Every two weeks the official publication for the Holstein breed, *The Holstein-Freisian World,* arrived at the Schlichting farm, and Mr. Schlichting always gave me the magazine when he and his son were through reading it. I took it home and read it over and over again until within a remarkably short time I was familiar with the great herds in both the United States and Canada. Maytag, Carnation, Pabst, Femco, Dunloggin, and Mount Victoria were magic names that I lived and breathed day and night.

A year or two previously, Henry Schlichting had purchased for $250 a purebred Holstein bull calf at a Wisconsin consignment sale. I had gone up to my neighbors to see this high-priced animal just as soon as he arrived at the farm. I have every reason to remember his name, Pabst Sir Cascade Mignonette. At first I was bewildered with these long, meaningless names which were given to registered animals, but they soon became very clear and interesting. In this particular case the bull had come from Pabst Farms, Oconomowoc, Wisconsin, one of the greatest herds of Ormsby-bred Holsteins in the world. The Ormsby line is one of the oldest and perhaps the strongest of the Holstein breed. Very few herds anywhere are without some of this blood. The name "Pabst" is a prefix or farm name registered in the

PART OF ARNEWOOD HERD IN PASTURE

CHECKING DAILY PRODUCTION AT ARNEWOOD

SHOCKED FODDER IN ARNEWOOD FIELD

FEEDING HOGS AT ARNEWOOD

Holstein-Friesian Association of America at Battleboro, Vermont, and is used exclusively by that farm to designate cattle bred by them. "Sir Cascade" comes from the sire of the calf. He was a son of Carnation Sensation, the great bull that Pabst Farms had purchased from Carnation Milk Farms, from their Cascade cow family. "Mignonette" represents the cow family from which the bull calf had come. At that time Pabst Farms were using a unique system of naming their females after flowers.

Pabst Sir Cascade Mignonette deserves a great deal of attention at this particular time because he proved to be one of the very greatest bulls ever used in Iowa, and because he was used so close to my own farm at the particular time when his services meant so much to the little herd that I was to build. It is noteworthy to mention that Mr. Schlichting was kind enough to allow me free service to this animal, without which I could not have achieved the results that came later. It was a tragic misfortune that this bull should have gone to the block before his worth was recognized. An index to a sire's real worth is computed by a comparison of the production records of his daughters over their own dams. This particular bull had an index of more than 520 pounds of butterfat in 305 days on twice-a-day milking. To illustrate just what this means: the average milch cow in the United States produces something in the neighborhood of 200 pounds fat in a year. This bull's daughters produced more than $2\frac{1}{2}$ times as much butterfat as the average dairy cow. Indexes are computed in 305 or 365 days, depending on how long the cow is run on test, and how often she is milked every day. Dairy cows are milked either twice, three times, or four times a day. The symbols 2x, 3x, and 4x are used to represent these divisions; for example, Betty produced 458 pounds fat in 305 days on 2x milking. It is expected cows will produce more milk the oftener they are milked. This varies among different individuals and under different farm conditions.

While I was shocking corn for my neighbor, one of his good registered cows dropped a heifer calf by the great Pabst bull. I was in the barn admiring the calf when my good friend, Henry Schlichting, came into the barn to bridle the horses for the afternoon's work on the corn binder. He saw me and walked over to the calfpen where I was, and in his usual abrupt manner, said, "You can have that calf for your wages if you want her."

My enthusiasm was spontaneous, "You really mean it?"

"Sure I do. You've shocked corn four days. The heifer is probably worth more than that, but you've helped us do other things; so you can have her. Your old Cutie is still giving enough milk for the house and enough to raise the calf, ain't she?"

"Oh, sure," I said, "she'll give enough for the calf."

"Say, Mel," he added, as an afterthought, but I figured out afterwards he had planned it with Fred, "bring up your Cutie and we'll take her to Pabst."

That was more than I had hoped for. We had always bred her to some beef bull; even then I hoped she would have a heifer calf. But if I could get a heifer calf out of her from Henry's great sire! Even my neighbor with his fine herd of purebreds realized that Cutie was a greater producer than anything he had, even though she was only a grade animal. Cutie did not get the ground feed that his cattle received, and I sometimes felt sad as I watched Henry's cows licking up their palatable feed and gorging themselves on the choice green alfalfa hay. If Cutie had the same feed and the same chance to be run on test as she deserved, I knew she could beat any cow that my neighbor had. How proud I was when I led Cutie home after she had been serviced to the great bull, and how hopeful!

The little heifer calf I received for my wages was named "Bessie," and was the first purebred I ever owned. She was recorded in the national breed register as "Jaquenetta Pabst Bessie." Stressing the importance of accuracy, Fred helped me mark off her color markings on the back of the application for registry, and fill out all the information necessary.

Bessie developed a navel infection which bothered her for some time. I kept doctoring it until it was completely healed. Another calamity fell shortly after I brought little Bessie home. For some reason Cutie dried up suddenly, and I had no milk for the calf. As usual I took my troubles to Mr. Schlichting. He didn't say anything for a while, then he turned to Fred.

"We're milking a lot of cows now. Couldn't we use a little help mornings? We'll give Mel enough skim milk for his calf, and a gallon of milk for the house if he wants to help us milk mornings. That will help us both out."

That proved agreeable all around; in fact, I helped them milk both morning and evening. And so Bessie ate and drank and grew.

I was a very lucky boy to have such a wonderful uncle as I had in my Uncle Dave. He did not live many miles away; sometimes he came over every day. One morning he drove into the yard with a trailer hitched behind his car. He called me from the barn yard, and I could see his face was all smiles.

"I had a couple bred gilts more'n I figured I needed for next spring. Can you use them, Mel?"

I jumped up on one of the wheels of the trailer and looked into the box. There were two big fat Duroc gilts.

"They're dandies!" I exclaimed joyfully. "Just what I needed, but I was afraid I couldn't afford any this year."

"Have you got a place for them?" Uncle Dave inquired, uncoupling the trailer from the car.

"The old shed south of the crib is empty," I said, putting my shoulder against the wagon and pushing while my uncle steered it against the loading chute. "We can drive them into that building and I can fix a pen for them later."

Uncle Dave walked up the chute and removed the endgate rods and boards. The two red gilts stepped daintily down the cleated ramp to the ground, their tails curled handsomely over their broad rumps. I ran ahead to open the gate while my uncle drove them through. As the hogs moved lackadaisically along, sniffing the earth with their flat snouts and flapping their wide ears out of their moronic eyes, their shoulders and hams weaved from side to side completely out of control.

"But I can't pay for them now," I said, with a feeling of concern, as the Durocs found the open shed door.

Uncle Dave laid his huge hand on my lean shoulder, his mouth and eyes beaming in a big broad grin, and replied, "They're yourn. You don't have to pay for them — ever."

Proudly I latched the door and walked back to the car with my uncle.

My uncle enjoyed coming over and helping me. He would go to the barn and look at Bessie and remark how fast she was growing, he would admire Cutie and my heart would swell with pride, he would tell me how to feed the gilts. Then when the winter came and there was time to get away for a few hours, he would take me to some of the farm auction sales in the county. He would look over a particular piece of machinery I was interested in buying, and tell me if there was anything wrong with it.

"This spreader needs a few new teeth in the beater," he said once, as we were inspecting a manure spreader that I needed badly, "but I can put them in some day when I'm over to your place in no time at all. It seems good otherwise. Buy it, Mel, if it don't go too high."

The crying and gesticulations of the auctioneer were always interesting, and every now and then he would make some amusing remark about an article he was selling that would bring a roar of laughter from the crowd, with a resultant acceleration of bidding. Holding up an old harness that was about ready to fall apart, he would say, "What am I bid for this harness? If you can't put it on your old nag, put it on your wife when you get home."

A conglomeration of useless articles was usually placed in a leaking bushel basket or empty nail keg and offered for sale — articles that if sold individually would not bring a cent.

"Look what we have here," the auctioneer cried, bringing forth a hammer without a handle from the grab bag of surprises, "a perfectly good tool. And the basket is full of goodies just like it."

A reverberant guffaw from the men, and perhaps a bid of fifty cents from somebody with enough gambling spirit to hope that the keg might contain a single worthwhile article.

With the first warm days in spring came the urge to plant and to work the soil. A new patch of strawberries was set out, and on the south side of the woodshed a hotbed was built in which cabbage and tomato seeds were planted. My uncle came over one afternoon in May with a Delicious apple tree. He planted it himself just east of the house overlooking the garden. I remember how carefully he dug the hole for the tree and arranged the roots in it; then he covered it up, gently packing the dirt around the tree. For weeks afterwards he took me over to the tree to see if it was growing. It was with a genuine feeling of achievement that my uncle watched the tiny sapling finally leaf out. I was always attentive to the tree, fearful that something might happen to it. I wanted it to live because it was a very personal gift from the man whose friendship I treasured above all others.

I had been counting the months, and then the weeks, and at last the days when Cutie would calve. June, the ideal month in the whole year for dairy cows because of its luscious grass, its invigorating warmth, and its freedom from flies, was the month destined for the never-to-be-forgotten event.

Cutie had never looked greater. Her udder was capacious and well attached, her mammary glands were large and tortuous, and her paunch deep and barreled. She was fat and in "show-ring bloom." I watched every day for the tailhead to drop, the one infallible indication that the cow was about to calve; then, when this sign appeared, I stayed by her day and night.

Late one afternoon Cutie began to become restless, and I understood. She wanted a place to have her calf. I made her a deep bed of dry straw in the shed west of the stable, and she followed me in. That was just what Cutie wanted, for she plunked herself right down in the middle of it with a deep sigh of uncomfortableness.

I was tired from lack of sleep and my whole body was weak with intense excitement and anticipation. Year after year she had dropped bull calves, and each time I had thought the law of averages would bring a heifer calf. This time I was more anxious than ever before, not only because she was carrying a calf sired by a proved bull, but also because I was starting my own herd and needed females.

I had not long to wait now. Cutie began laboring, and in a matter of minutes the calf was born. I quickly removed the membrane from the face of the helpless form. It shook its head, its wet ears flapping against its face; and its warm body started throbbing with the breath of new life. Cutie got to her feet and turned around to see what had caused all the excitement. Excitement it was indeed, for this time she began to lick a fine heifer calf!

"Cutie!" I cried with joy, and threw my arms around her neck. "You've done it! You've done it!"

Cutie was too busy attending her calf to take any credit for the event. After getting her some warm water to drink, I went over to Schlichtings to tell them the good news.

"Now I suppose you'll be counting the days until the heifer calf is old enough to freshen," Henry commented with a smile.

"Yes, sir," I replied. "I'll want to see what kind of a producer she'll be."

Before going to bed that night, I went again to the shed to see Cutie and her heifer calf. I sat by my cow, just looking at her and the little heifer, until it got so dark I could no longer see. The calf had filled its stomach, and, satisfied, had snuggled close against its mother. Happy beyond all comprehension, I left the shed and went to the house.

I was up next morning with the sun before anyone else in the house was awake. I slipped into my clothes, ran down the stairs, and outside to look at Cutie and her heifer. I opened the shed door and stopped, the very blood in my veins running cold. For just an instant all I could do and say was to stand there, horrified, and gasp the name "Cutie!"

Cutie was lying stretched out on the straw, her head to one side. That was all I saw then. That is all I waited to see. I had never seen a case of milk fever before, but I had heard so much about it that I knew instantly what was the matter with Cutie. I did not stop to find out if she was alive. I just kept saying to myself that she wasn't dead, that she couldn't die. I rushed back to the house and called the veterinarian. I remember telling him to hurry, that it was milk fever. I needn't have said that much, for he could tell by my voice and the words "milk fever" that there was no time to lose. Actually, he was at the farm in fifteen minutes from the time I called, and he lived seven miles away; but those minutes were hours as I waited by my cow for him to come.

Although I discovered after further investigation that Cutie was still alive, I realized there was very little life in her. The bewildering stages of the coma when she must have staggered around before falling to the ground, bruising her head and body on the brick wall, were past. Blood was still oozing from these cuts. There was only an occasional tonic spasm of the muscles of the neck now, no groans. If I could only help her! If only I could do something for her! Those were the only thoughts that kept racing in my mind. Frantically I rubbed her cold legs. That was all I could think of doing: to rub circulation back into those extremities.

At last the veterinarian came. He saw the situation at once, and went to work. I knew he was worried, too, because he said nothing but kept working feverishly over the cow. There was not enough pulse left any longer to find the jugular vein at once. Only after several nerve-shattering efforts with the needle did the small red drops of blood begin to trickle slowly out of the needle. A bottle of calcium gluconate was inverted, the tube connected to the needle in the vein, and the contents began to flow into the blood stream.

There were tears in my eyes and I could not see the liquid disappearing from the bottle. I did not care. I could not help it. Yet the one all-possessing thought "She will not die!" persisted.

Then the veterinarian removed the apparatus from the needle, jerked the needle out of the vein, rubbed the area for a minute, raised himself up and sighed. Once it seemed the breathing was coming faster. There were little twitchings of the muscles, and my hopes fairly soared. The seeming signs of returning strength and life were occasioned only by the powerful stimulant in the blood stream, but the heart was already too weak to cope with it.

With one last convulsive gasp the noble animal that had meant more to me than anything else in life breathed her last. Even in that terrible moment I could not believe she was dead. But the realization came, and I sank down against her, the last remaining ounce of my own strength slipping away with the life of the thing I loved. Tenderly I held the lifeless head in my arms. The tears were coming unrestrainedly now, and I kept whispering her name over and over again, hoping still that by some miracle those kind, liquid eyes would open once more and speak to me as only they could. But they were closed forever, and with them a boy's eyes that would never open again to see the things that boys see, to feel the things that boys feel.

I did not notice when the veterinarian left. With tender understanding he had slipped unnoticed from the shed, his duties performed. I believed at that moment that my whole future, with every ambition and hope, was as lifeless as the animal that had sustained them.

I relived in those agonizing moments that followed all the scenes with Cutie that had ever been. I saw her as she first looked in the pasture that sunny day in August when my father gave her to me, the frightening black and white heifer; saw her eating grass in the pasture, drinking from the tank, chewing her cud under the trees; sensed the thrill of a cool summer rain soothing her throbbing body; felt the tingle of the chase as she played hide-and-seek with me in the cornfield; drifted with her into that vast expanse of sky and air and sunshine in the world that was hers, the world she loved so well; experienced the bitter winter winds, the driving snow and sleet she was forced to endure, the gnawing hunger that made it worse.

The leaves on the trees, green with life in spring and summer, turn brown and gold in the autumn, fluttering to the ground — only to be replaced more gloriously in the springtime. The flowers that bloom with such brilliance in the warm months are doomed to wither and die, but within those dry and withered blossoms lie tiny seeds with unborn life in them — promises of a repetition of the mother bloom in the endless cycle that is life and death.

The new-born heifer calf, forgotten in that awful transition, now began to feel the first pangs of hunger and started to its feet in search of food, for which its own limited experience had already taught it to go to its mother's udder. It nuzzled the old cow's lifeless form and let out a plaintive bleat upon receiving no response, its wobbly, crooked legs buckling beneath it.

I turned and looked at it. I should have resented it for what it had done. But in my mind the truth was shaping. Its own helplessness touched me deeply, and in its innocent baby face I saw only Cutie, and my heart cried out for it, and my arms went out to it, and, drawing it closer, encircled it.

Part Two

Arnewood

* VI *

Holsteins and Durocs

ONE THING became clear in my mind after Cutie died. She had taught me that a great love for one animal does not die with it; that once a man becomes attached to a great cow, his love for good cattle can never be destroyed. That is the only reason why a good dairyman can triumph over all the disappointments that are sure to beset him.

I decided to stay by my cattle. It has been truly said that "Once a Holstein man, always a Holstein man." I determined to build one of the finest herds in the county, and some day I would find an animal that would measure up to the one I had lost. I would search for her and wait; never would I be satisfied until I had found her. Then when I had found her, I would feed and care for her the best way I knew how, and in this way make up to Cutie for what she had missed in life. Cutie never had the chance to make a great record, as a cow of her rare producing ability should have had; but some day, after I had found a cow worthy, I would prove to myself and to my pet what she might have done.

It is not easy to get into the purebred business. It takes money and courage, determination and perseverance. In addition, to become successful with a herd of dairy cows, four prime requisites are necessary: good cows, good feed, good management, and a certain amount of good luck. Try to build a profitable herd without all these, and see what happens.

I was lucky from the start in my new enterprise. Of course the little heifer that Cutie had left was only a grade animal, but she would stay in the herd regardless. She would always be the favorite. I called her Snooks. And because Bessie, the first registered Holstein in my herd, had the distinction of growing up with Cutie, she received Cutie's old stanchion. The first year I managed to save enough money, after the rent for the farm had been paid, to purchase a foundation cow from my neighbor, Mr. Schlichting. The cow selected was a black cow named Stella. I paid $110 for her and her day-old heifer calf that I later named Lily. In time Bessie dropped her first calf, and I was again fortunate in getting another heifer, Lassie Maid.

I persuaded my landlord to put a cement floor and a gutter in the dairy barn. In order to remodel the old stable a compromise was reached between us. The owner of the farm agreed to cement the rear of the stable, including the gutter, to within two feet of the stanchions. That space was left as a dirt floor, but was probably easier in the long run for the cows to lie on. I was to install the steel stanchions at my own expense, while the landlord was to furnish wooden boxes in front of each stall instead of the usual cement feed trough. Now at last the dairy barn was comfortable for the cows.

All this time the services of the Pabst bull were costing me nothing, and I was getting some very fine heifer calves without the great cost and trouble of keeping a herd sire of my own. This saving enabled me to add females to my herd faster than would otherwise have been possible. Even with this master stroke of good fortune, I was not financially able to buy the best cows in my neighbor's herd as I should have liked to; but in every case I was successful in selecting cows that became good brood matrons.

The second foundation animal purchased was a two-year-old heifer that proved to be the best transmitting cow developed in my herd. She was registered in the Holstein-Friesian Herd Books as Princess Ormsby Marathon Bessie. She has had offspring go to many fine herds, including a son to the leading dairy in Florida for a four-figure price. Princess died in the late fall of 1950 at past fourteen years of age.

The purchase of this great animal was interesting in many respects. When I walked into my neighbor's barn one afternoon in January, the heifer in question was under lively discussion. Fred had just finished milking her, but the milk that should have been in his pail was dripping from his blue jacket and overalls like a fresh seven-minute icing that should have been boiled a little longer. This exasperated young man was calling Princess some very undesirable names, and was threatening to land a blow on her trembling rump with a milk-stool fashioned from a block of wood with a handle on the side. The heifer was looking around nervously, her eyes filled with fear and excitement; and in her frustration she shoved the cow next to her with her rear end, almost upsetting Mr. Schlichting, who was milking her.

"That's the last straw!" the older man shouted, as he got up from his stool with a bucket of milk brimming over with foam. "Princess goes on the block tomorrow! Can't have kickers around here. Besides, she doesn't give any milk anyway."

"What's all the trouble?" I asked.

"Everything's the trouble!" Fred answered gruffly. "The dang fool kicks every time she's milked. I'm the only one that'll milk her any more, and I quit as of now."

"Did I hear you say you were going to sell her?" I asked Henry. "She's too fine an animal to sell on the market."

The heifer was more white than black, large for her age, straight as a string over the topline, with scale and style to spare. She was unquestionably the most outstanding individual for type in my neighbor's entire string of cows. I had always admired her, and now I was determined to own her.

"She's typy all right," Henry commented, "but she's for sale."

"I came up this afternoon looking for another cow," I said. "How much will you take for Princess?"

"You don't mean you really want to buy her, Mel?" Fred stared at me with disbelief.

"I most certainly do!" I reaffirmed. "How much?"

"How much?" Mr. Schlichting echoed, setting his pail down, and scratching his forehead. "Well, Mel, you know what she is, but if you think you can handle her, she's yours for a hundred dollars."

"Fair enough," I agreed. "I'll buy her. I'm not afraid of her."

By this time the excitement was over, and Princess was munching her hay along with the rest of the cows. The calves in another part of the barn could hear the rattle of the milk pails, and knowing that feeding time was near, let out a weird chorus of bawls and squeals; one calf had been bleating so long that it had become hoarse and could only give a shrill little squeak.

Both Fred and his father laughed at me for my choice, but they were too happy over the prospect of being rid of Princess to offer much argument; besides, I think they were a little curious to see what she would do in her new home. They decided that as long as the heifer had never had a halter on before, we should not try to lead her down to my place, but rather drive her down the road with a group of their young heifers. This we did, and finally managed to get her into the barn lot. Princess was holding her head high, her eyes were flashing, and her long white switch was poised in mid-air; every muscle and fiber in her beautiful body was alive, and she resembled more a prize Hackney than a dairy heifer. I opened the barn door and she made a dash through the opening.

For a few days afterwards, whenever I left her out in the lot with the rest of the herd for exercise, my neighbors had to come down to help me get her back into the barn. The first times I milked her, she kicked the pail clear across the barn; then she would turn around to see what I would do. I did not scold or whip her, and I think she was disappointed. That seemed to take the thrill out of it for her, and she grew tired of kicking. Be that as it may, within a week or two I could milk her anywhere outside in the yard; and I shall never forget the dismay on the faces of Fred and his father when shortly after I bought the heifer I led her into their yard. Princess handled like a champion at the halter, and looked every inch the part.

Of the manner of breaking this heifer, Fred used to say, "I believe

Princess could have kicked Mel against the barn wall, breaking a rib or two, and he'd get up and pet her."

About this time I decided the herd should have a prefix. Several names were suggested by the breed association, and the name "Arnewood" was at last chosen. It belonged exclusively to the cattle I bred.

I was in luck once more when a few days before Christmas, Princess gave birth to a large, beautifully marked heifer calf. She was one to remember, one that lived but a few short years; yet in those years she achieved lasting greatness. Her name was short and as charming as the animal herself — Arnewood Amy. My Uncle Dave was in the barn with me when Princess dropped this valuable Christmas present. He was there with me more and more frequently, sharing every little triumph and fretting over every little worry of the herd, watching it grow with an interest only slightly less than my own.

After this initial run of heifer calves, my luck changed and bull calves became the rule; yet I had had the heifers when I really needed them, and they were growing up to build my herd. I now had six purebreds. They had cost me $210, an inestimable amount of sweat and toil, and a generous amount of pride and joy.

Baby Snooks grew, too, and learned every mischievous prank of her illustrious namesake. Not at all like her beautiful dam, Snooks was gangly and slopy-rumped. With me she had every confidence and behaved like a kitten; but to strangers she acted as fierce as any wild beast. At the mere sight of a visitor she was off to the far corner of the pasture, her head high and her eyes filled with fear and hatred. Seeing her in these moods reminded me of Cutie's behavior when I had first known her. But Snooks went further. Even my uncle who was in the barn almost every day with her was like a stranger to her, and she would stop eating and tremble all over until he left the barn.

Mr. Schlichting watched her and shook his head. "I'm afraid she's going to disappoint you someday. She's an outlaw, that's what she is! Probably never will give any milk."

"But she's got to be a good producer," I insisted. "Her mother was."

"I'm sorry, Mel, but I'm afraid that makes no difference," he explained. "Cutie was one of those cows that we call sports. One of those cows that you see only once in a lifetime. She was great herself, but was unable to transmit any of her own great ability."

"Still and all," I promised, "I'm not going to give up hope in her yet."

"She's going to have to do a lot of changin' before I see any good in her," my friend said, shaking his head. "How are the pigs doing?" he asked, dismissing the subject of Snooks.

"Come over and I'll show them to you," I suggested eagerly. "They're a healthy looking bunch."

Mr. Schlichting followed me to the alfalfa meadow east of the buildings where I had a four-pen hog house with a gambrel roof. I had purchased it early that spring already built on skids so that it could be easily moved from one part of the field to another. Newly painted white with green-trimmed windows, it was very attractive. Since I had had no hog house on the farm previously, this new building enabled me to keep four bred gilts from the two litters I had raised the year before from the sows my uncle had given me.

Because I did not have the equipment and buildings necessary to rear successfully two litters every year, I arranged to have my gilts farrow during the last days in April or early May when the weather would be mild and the pasture abundant. The four gilts had finished farrowing and their six-to-nine-pig litters were just at that stage about ten days after birth when their little pink and black bodies were fat and wrinkly from the abundantly filled nipples of their mothers. The young sows were snoozing on their bellies with their pigs dozing in the straw around them in their individual pens when we entered the building.

"You got some nice litters, Mel," Mr. Schlichting said, looking over the lot with an appraising eye. "You've got a fine place for them, too. They've got to be on clean ground to be thrifty."

"Yes, I know," I answered with the conviction of a veteran hog raiser. "About all they need now is lots of pasture and skim milk, and they are getting it, too."

"Go easy on the skim milk for a while," my friend warned. "If the sows get too much the pigs'll scour."

The little pigs woke up when they heard us talking, stretched themselves, and began squealing and pushing their pink noses against the stiff bristly sides of the sows, who responded with grunts of invitation and rolled over on their sides, but otherwise did not bother to open their eyes or flap their ears out of them so they could see. Their little families clambered over them like Lilliputians, and began nursing as

DISPERSAL SCENES OF ARNEWOOD HERD

BULL CARNATION ILLUSTRATOR IN AUCTION RING

FRED AND HENRY SCHLICHTING (*extreme right*) AT DISPERSAL SALE

1. MAGGIE BEETS CASCADE   2. PRINCESS ORMSBY MARATHON BESSIE

3. ARNEWOOD AMY

if their very lives depended on it, as, in truth, they did. Some of the pigs bit each other in their struggle over the extra papillae.

"You'll be marketing them, I suppose, after the first of the year," Mr. Schlichting mused, rubbing his back against the inside of the door.

"Sooner than that," I corrected, pleased all over with the thought of beating him to market with my hogs. "Around the first of December. They'll be seven months old then."

"And you're going to tell me that they're going to average 250 pounds when you sell them!" he teased.

"No, I'm not," I replied. "They're going to average 280 pounds!"

"Ha! Ha!" he laughed. "You've set your goal too high this time."

"Just how much do you bet I can't do it?" I asked, determined to call his bluff.

"Ten dollars says you can't get them up to 280 pounds in seven months!" he said seriously, gesturing for my hand. "Here, shake on it. You realize that to get that average some of your pigs'll have to weigh over 300 pounds?"

"They will," I promised, and we left the hog house, my friend shaking his head back and forth.

"You've made a bad bargain that time," he said.

I had long ago decided that it was much easier to raise hogs than chickens. I did not like hogs nearly as well as I did the chickens, but I soon found that with my time so completely taken up with the dairy cows and the regular field work, I could not devote the hours to raising chickens that were required. With hogs I did not have the constant cleaning and disinfecting of the floors and feeders and waterers as with baby chicks; no day-and-night vigil over them to see that they would not crowd and smother; nor the ever-present fear of disease sweeping through them and killing every last one of them.

I bred my Duroc gilts to a Spotted Poland China boar. I found that these cross-bred pigs developed faster than purebreds and, like hybrid chickens, were more resistant to disease. I could put them on clean ground, wean them, clean out their house once every two weeks or longer if I didn't get around to it, throw out a little corn for them twice a day, and feed them the skim milk after I separated. That is all the work they required, and they grew like weeds.

There isn't any young animal on the farm as sweet and loving as a little pig when it is a few weeks old; but it soon outgrows its charm. If it had not been for the fact that they grew so alarmingly fast with so little attention, and that the money they would bring in the fall meant so much to the successful operation of the farm, I am sure there were times when I should have vowed not to raise a pig at all.

I simply dreaded feeding them skim milk. I had a large wooden trough with strips of wood nailed every foot or so across the top to keep the pigs from getting in and splashing the milk out. For a time I was able to pour the milk in the trough from both ends, but as the pigs got older, they became wiser and beat me to every move I could make. I planned and schemed for hours on end how I could out-maneuver those rascals, but each time I fed them they managed to waste about half the milk.

Fred suggested that I cut a square hole in the fence, pull the trough through about a foot or so, giving me room to pour the milk without the hogs bothering me. The first time I tried this they piled on top of one another and broke the fence down. The next day I fixed that. I built a fence over the trough out of planks and two-by-fours, cer-tain now that I should have no more trouble feeding them milk. But oh, how wrong I was. True, they could not break down my barri-cade, but they did pile up at the mouth-end of the trough and dam the milk so it could not get through.

Finally, in desperation, I purchased a second trough. I figured I could pour a little milk in one of the troughs, thereby luring the van-dals to it while I slipped unnoticed to the second trough, which I could leisurely fill. But this worked just a few times. The hogs had a brain I had not counted on. They figured it out, and were at the second trough ahead of me.

One evening after an especially hard day shocking corn I was late with my chores, and the hogs were hungrier than usual by the time I had finished the separating. I had four tall cans of skim milk near the fence to give them. I straddled the fence, reached back for the first can and made a dash for the first trough. I poured enough into it to attract the hogs to it, then ran with my can of milk for the second trough and succeeded in dumping the contents into it. I went back for a second can and filled the first trough. Anxious to get the job over, I grabbed the last two cans, one in each hand, and made for one of the troughs that seemed free from hogs. But the greedy swine had already emptied both troughs, and were coming at me from both directions. Determined to outsmart them, I held the cans higher and pushed through. I was almost ahead of them, and confident of winning the race, when a big shoat, whether by accident or design I shall never know, made a beeline between my running legs, and all pandemonium broke loose. I spraddled headfirst in the filthy muck, one can of milk falling on top of me, the other being carried several yards on the back of a runaway hog before it emptied on the ground in a wide white pool. The hogs were swooshing up the milk wherever they could get to it, and further contaminating me and my clothes by running over me. I managed to get up and salvage the muddy dented cans from the havoc, when I saw Fred standing on the other side of the fence, laughing as if it were the funniest sight he had ever seen. I would have burst into tears had I not been so infuriated.

"You — you — !" I cried, unable to find a word to express my feelings. "Stop laughing at me!"

Fred laughed all the harder. "So this is your method of raising 280-pound hogs in seven months!"

"I declare, Fred," I warned, recovering from my discomfiture, "if you don't stop teasing me, I'll — I'll beat you to a pulp!"

"You'd laugh, too, if you found me in such a predicament," he said, offering to relieve me of the cans. "You'd better go to the house and clean up. I'll see you tomorrow."

When it rained the hogs began rooting in the alfalfa, and wallowing in the mud puddles. They even raised the hog-tight fences with their snouts and got out on the road. I was forced to put rings in their noses, a task which did not bother me in the least, and to stretch a barbwire along the ground all along the fence.

They continued to gain weight, and when the new corn was ready to pick in the fall, I snapped some every day for them, gradually increasing the amount until they had corn before them all the time. The evenings began to grow cooler and I had to watch them for fear they would lie outdoors and catch colds. I was glad to see them go to market on the first day in December, and as soon as I received the weight slip from the packing company I took it up for Mr. Schlichting to see. The hogs had averaged a little more than 284 pounds!

☆ VII ☆

Building the Arnewood Herd

It had always been my desire to own a heifer from the famous Maytag herd at Newton, Iowa. By 1940 I was able to fulfill this dream. During State Fair week, in August, Judy, my cousin Miriam, and I made the trip to Newton in Judy's Model A Ford coupe to visit the farm and to inspect two heifers that had been offered for sale.

This trip was one that I shall long remember; it was the first time that I had taken the liberty to leave the work at home to travel so far. Actually the distance was only 110 miles, but for me that was a long trip. Oliver, who was working out on a farm near Mason City, was able to get the day off and do the chores for me while I was away. It was drizzling when we left home, but before noon the rain stopped, and the sun came out bright and clear.

Newton is the seat of Jasper County, and typifies the growth of manufacturing in a state traditionally and predominantly agricultural. The business district is built around a square which is dominated by a three-story courthouse. Hundreds of factory workers, going to and from work, and great numbers of farmers milling around the square portray the city's dual character. This city is the leading manufacturing place in the world for washing machines. The industry was founded in the 1890's, and under the leadership of F. L. Maytag, who became known as the "Washing Machine King," it grew by leaps and bounds.

It was E. H. Maytag, the son of F. L. Maytag, who started the Maytag herd of registered Holsteins as a hobby. The main dairy farm is located about a mile north of Newton. The set of gleaming white buildings with their green roofs and the beautifully landscaped yards, attractively located on the south side of a small hill in a valley, make this place one of the most beautiful of its kind in the world.

I had never seen anything like it, and my heart pounded furiously when I caught my first glimpse of it from the top of the ridge overlooking the farmstead. As we drove into the yard, Mr. M. M. Campbell, the able manager, was just leaving the office. He greeted us warmly, and I introduced myself, my sister, and Miriam. When he tipped his hat, I noticed that his bald head was in sharp contrast to his otherwise youthful appearance. Mr. Campbell was a small, clean-shaven man, dressed in smart business apparel. He wore a pair of rimless glasses, and each time before he spoke he cleared his throat. As we walked through the barns, and he pointed out many of the large, sleek, black and white creatures that were already familiar to me by name from the advertisements I had read on the inside cover of the *World,* I became aware that this hawking was a peculiar habit of Mr. Campbell's.

The interior of the dairy barns was completely modern: individual watering cups, concrete feeding troughs, ventilators with thermostatically controlled electric fans to force fresh air into the buildings, ceiling fans over each of the box stalls which were constructed of tubular steel panels, electrified screens to kill flies, windows with green awnings, and cork-brick floors. Each test cow received a box stall to herself, to allow her complete freedom to move about as she pleased. What a far cry this was from the little barn that housed my own cows!

Miriam was more surprised at the striking surroundings than Judy or I, and made comments now and then. "These cows have it nicer than most people!" she would say.

"Mr. Maytag loved his cows," our guide informed us. "Nothing was too good for them. He died this summer, you know." There was a break in his voice as he spoke, and I felt the close bond that had existed between them.

After a tour of the buildings, Mr. Campbell showed us the two heifers I was interested in. Each had had one calf and was carrying her second. Satisfied that they were as good as I had pictured them, I decided to buy them; and, as I handed the manager a check for four hundred dollars for the two animals, I felt I had transacted a big business deal. I was assured the heifers would be delivered safe and sound to my farm within a few days. As we walked back to the car, which was parked near the office, I watched the office door close on Mr. Campbell's tweed-covered back, little realizing the importance this man was to assume in my later life.

We packed ourselves in the Model A and started for Des Moines and the State Fair, the first time any of us had ever visited it. It was about an hour's drive from Newton to the east edge of Des Moines, where the State Fair Grounds were located. The drive, around many curves and through rugged, hilly terrain, was very beautiful. Not having been to the state capital or to the State Fair before, we experienced some difficulty finding the fairgrounds; but once in the vicinity of the agricultural and industrial show, made famous some years previous by Phil Stong in his novel, we could hear the familiar sounds of the fair and shortly we saw the main entrances, with colored banners waving their welcomes from the tops of the several gates.

We parked the car outside of the grounds, paid our admissions, and hurried inside. The riot of colors and sounds was exhilarating. There were so many people hurrying to and fro that I offered each of the girls a hand in order to keep us all together. There was so much to see and so little time in which to see it that we had to make every moment count.

To make matters worse we discovered that each of us wanted to see something different. Judy wanted to see the school exhibits, while

Miriam suggested she would like to visit the WHO radio broadcasting tent. And of course I was fairly itching to get to the livestock barns.

"We'll see what you girls want to see first," I compromised. "Then you'll have to come with me to see the cattle."

"Agreed," chimed the girls, as arm-in-arm we danced along the cement walks from one attraction to another.

"Gee, this makes our county fair look awfully small!" I remarked, much impressed by the size of the show and the number of the concessions.

"And imagine, cement walks instead of that dusty old midway!" Miriam said, as we walked beneath the quaint elm trees that grew so beautifully all over the grass-covered fairgrounds.

The rural school educational exhibits were the first on our agenda. They were interesting at first even to Miriam and me; but when Judy took out her pencil and notebook and began a detailed examination of each booth (there was one from each of the ninety-nine counties in the state), taking down every new idea she saw, Miriam and I decided despairingly that we would have to spend the entire afternoon there. After what seemed an eternity, Judy closed her little book, filled I believed with enough new ideas for all the rural teachers of Cerro Gordo County for the next year, and turned to us and said, oh so sweetly, "There! I'm finished. Didn't take very long, did I, Melvin?"

After that we located the radio tent, and upon learning it would be a full hour before the next broadcast, we decided to take in the dairy barns and then return for the radio program.

The cattle barns were some distance from the other buildings, and we lost some time in finding them. I should have liked to spend all the time I had in the dairy barns, but I remembered that the girls were patiently tagging along merely to oblige me, so I hurried as fast as possible. This was my first experience seeing show cattle on the big-time circuit. Several of the big herds from other states were at the Iowa show, proudly announcing themselves from great signs posted above their strings of well-groomed, blanketed animals. Some of the booths were gayly decorated with green bunting and red roses.

"We might as well leave him here, Miriam, and go back to the WHO tent," Judy said, glancing at her wristwatch.

"Is it time for the broadcast?" I asked in surprise. "Have we been here that long?"

"The way you've been looking, I don't think you've even been conscious!" Miriam said smilingly.

"Let's go then," I said, and led the way back to the radio tent. After the radio show was over, we ate hot dogs and drank strawberry pop at a stand on the midway. When the night crowd came, the gay lights of the merry-go-round, the ferris wheel, and many other rides, the eating places, the game stands, and the side shows turned the sky into a brilliant spectacle of light and color. Above the gay lilt of the calliope, and the hullabaloo of the crowd, the barkers shouted their invitations: "Right this way to see the man with the disappearing stomach"; "Take a chance on the lucky wheel"; "Here's a husky young man who wants to swing the sledge and ring the bell"; "Your choice of any of these valuable prizes if I fail to guess your weight within three pounds"; "Closer, gentlemen, and watch Fifi dance. This is just a sample of what you'll see on the inside."

We rode on the ferris wheel, we stopped at the weight guessing booth where I won a Kewpie doll for Miriam, and we ate candy floss until Judy suggested that it was time to leave the fair. On the way home, I experienced a feeling of relief and happiness for this brief interlude of fun, and looked forward with a fresh hope and inspiration to the more serious business awaiting me at Arnewood.

Now that I had a select foundation herd started, my next step was to join the local Dairy Herd Improvement Association to which all progressive dairymen in the county belonged. How I hoped that someday my own herd would lead all the herds in the county for production of butterfat. My friend, Mr. Schlichting, was not surprised when I told him one day that I planned to put my herd on test. There would be a friendly rivalry between us now, since his herd had long been recognized not only as the best herd in the county, but one of the oldest as well. The Schlichting herd had just made an average butterfat record of a little over 400 pounds, which is an enviable goal to reach.

"It took Fritzie and me seventeen years to accomplish this, Mel," he said, "so don't be discouraged if you don't do so well the first year."

"But you had to build your herd," I argued. "You had to cull your low producers. I shall have an advantage over you in that I have been fortunate in being able to buy some of your animals without waiting the years it takes to breed cows with great inherent production. I want to make a four-hundred-pound herd average, but I just can't wait seventeen years."

"Well, Mel," my friend said, flicking some imaginary lint from his sleeve, "we shall see. I know better than to make any rash bets with you!"

In this manner the foundation herd at Arnewood was made. Determination and a certain amount of beginner's luck had made this possible. It was not all so easy as it might sound. There was never an exorbitant amount spent for foundation cows; yet the addition of each cow to the herd meant perhaps a year's work of raising crops and hogs, a year's amount of sweat and backbreaking toil, of pinching every penny, of depriving myself of momentary pleasures and amusements, and of lying awake nights planning and worrying a little, too. But the reward of owning another brood cow was well worth all the effort.

There were other things that had to be bought. There was the matter of purchasing a horse and a few pieces of machinery, seed for planting, and feed for the cows, poultry, and hogs. The acquisition of a new cream separator alone required great frugality.

It was good to plan for the herd. I had ample time for this as I mowed the hay and put it in cocks; or spread manure over the stubble field; or rode the one-row cultivator down the checked corn rows, dust from the wheels blowing in my face. Then when the long day's work in the field was done, there was the pleasant task of milking; for no matter how hard I might have worked or how tired I might be, it was a delightful relaxation to sit down to milk the fine, well-fed milch cows that were waiting for me.

To me there was nothing drab about life at Arnewood. Each day was filled with something interesting and worth while. And I was not alone in struggling ahead. Mother was there, always doing more than her share when she was able. Of course she no longer planted the acre or more of garden vegetables that she had grown on the forty even back in the days when we had lived in town. There was no longer any need for such a large garden. Except on week ends and summer vacations when Judy and Eldena came home — Eldena was staying with our aunt in town and going to high school — and during the winter months when Father was not able to work with the construction outfit, Mother and I were home alone. Oliver sometimes came on Sundays.

Mother took care of the hens. We did not keep many of these. I liked the hybrids better than the purebreds for the reason that they were hardier, grew faster, and laid better. I had chosen the White Rock-Leghorn cross. In addition, I usually bought fifty Light Brahma cockerels and caponized them myself. This breed is the largest of all breeds of chickens, and the caponized birds if kept over one year sometimes weigh up to eighteen pounds. A peculiar characteristic of these capons is that they have a fondness for baby chicks, and make excellent brooders, being able with their great size and abundance of soft breast feathers to cover about thirty chicks.

Occasionally I was the tragi-comic victim of my own try for perfection. There was the time I dug the new hole back of the woodshed for the outhouse. I was determined to do a good job of it; so I carefully measured it and dug it square and deep. The work took an entire forenoon and when I had finished digging, I called Mother out to look at my masterpiece of excavation.

"Stop me from my work just to look at this!" she said, pretending to be angry, as she wiped her hands on her pretty print apron made from a feed sack. "It is a fine hole, though, but do be careful not to rub against the French lilac with the horse."

"I won't," I promised her as she started back to the kitchen to prepare our dinner. "Shall I hitch up Prince before dinner and finish the job or wait till this afternoon?"

"Better come on in to dinner first," she called back from the house. "It may take you longer than you think when you get started, and I don't want dinner to get cold."

After dinner I hurried out of the house to hitch up the old blind horse. I figured Prince would work better than the old mare, because I knew she would be frightened and would shy away from the hole. I fastened a length of hay rope around the building and tied it to the singletree, and placed my hand on the horse's bridle.

"Come ahead, Prince," I said, and he started pulling the small building.

Everything went along smoothly until the horse came opposite the hole. He stopped for a minute, and therein lies the tragedy. For when he started pulling again, the straining against the load caused the soft earth to give way, and I saw Prince slipping over the edge. I shouted for him to go ahead, and held fast to his bridle, hoping that he would make just one more step ahead to safety. Prince obeyed;

but the extra effort only made matters worse, and the whole side caved in. The horse fell into the hole, and nearly dragged me down with him.

The hole was ruined. I could see that. So I decided that I could make it no worse by digging some more. Maybe I could dig the horse out. I dug and dug and dug. After I had tunneled through into the garden, I slapped the horse gently across the neck. Instantly he lunged forward, but the more he tried to get up, the more securely did he become wedged in the hole.

There was but one thing left to do: hitch up the old mare and pull Prince out by the neck. When I had the old girl hitched up and the rope tied around the neck of the blind horse, I discovered there was not room enough in the lilac patch to drive ahead; so I had to chop out Mother's favorite lilac. I grabbed the mare's bridle and urged her ahead. She balked, and nothing I could do would encourage her to pull.

In the meantime it started to rain, and I do mean rain. The water began to rise in the hole, and I became alarmed lest the horse drown if he wasn't rescued soon.

"Mother! Mother!" I called, and finally she came out with a coat thrown over her head.

"Oh, dear!" she cried, taking in the situation at once. "What are you going to do now?"

"Call Fred Benn and tell him I've got a horse in a hole. He'll know what to do," I said. "And tell him to hurry!"

Mother rushed back to the house and I waited. The drenching rain was running off the back of the mare like a small waterfall, and the steam from her body resembled the spume from a cataract. She shook her lowered head in disgust. My clothes were soaked completely and clung as tightly to my body as a bathing suit.

Suddenly a car sloshed into the yard, and Fred Benn jumped out, holding a shotgun in his right hand. When he saw the blind horse in the hole with just his head sticking out and me struggling desperately and hopelessly with the mare to get him out, Mr. Benn stopped and began laughing until I thought he would die.

"What's the shotgun for?" I asked, unable to see anything funny in the situation.

My neighbor reached back and laid the gun on the car seat, slammed the door shut, and came toward me, still guffawing loudly.

"When your mother said you had a horse in a hole I thought it fell in a hole in the field and broke its leg. I was going to shoot it."

Fred examined the rope around Prince's neck, adjusted it, and picked up a switch from the ground.

"There's no reason why the mare shouldn't pull him right out," he said. "Hold her straight ahead." I pulled on her bridle.

"Geedup!" Fred Benn shouted to the mare, and whacked her across the rump.

The mare jumped forward. The blind horse felt the jerk on the rope and stumbled to his feet. The mare was pulling steadily now, and Prince struggled out of the hole.

"There! That's all there is to it," Fred said, helping me unhitch the horses and lead them to the barn. "We didn't need the shotgun after all."

I could laugh, too, now that my predicament was over and the humor of the situation presented itself.

* VIII *

Threshing Time

THERE WAS one time of year when the routine schedule of milking was interrupted — threshing time. Because I could buy oats cheaper than I could raise them, I seldom put in more than a few acres and then only as a nurse crop for new seedings of grasses and legumes for pasture. For this reason I did not belong to the regular threshing run. I did, however, help out half a dozen neighbors, who in turn helped harvest my small grain.

In normal years the oats were sown in early April. Mr. Schlichting taught me to count off nine rows of corn stubble for each round of the seeder so that there would be an even stand. The oats were first sown, then disked in. After that, the smaller seeds of clovers, alfalfa, and timothy were broadcast over the field. With these tinier seeds the distance for each swath was shorter because the seeds did not scatter so far as the oats. The grass and legume seeds were not disked in because they might be covered too deeply. When brome grass, a variety that was just being introduced in our county at that time, was planted, it was necessary to sow it with the oats on account of its being so very light. The field was then dragged several times to make a smooth seedbed. At first I had always walked behind the drag as the slow team made infinitesimal, scalloped designs across the black, dusty field. Year after year I had envied my neighbors as they literally sped across their fields, riding their tractors. Fred suspected that I was getting old and lazy one spring when I hitched a drag cart behind the harrow so I could ride. Some of my neighbors had culti-packers they used to roll over the new seedbed to pack the soil more firmly and to hold the moisture at the surface, thus aiding the seeds to sprout more rapidly.

In a few weeks the oats were up, and if the usual rains came, there would be a luscious pasture by late May. The cows were turned out on it unless the soil was so wet that the cattle's feet would beat the tender shoots into the ground. They would graze eagerly on this early spring pasture. In a few days the cows would have the new seeding browsed close to the ground, and they would have to be taken off. Such clipping of the oats at this time enabled them to stool, and resulted in a greater yield at harvest time.

By late June the oats were headed out, and under the hot July sun turned into a sea of churning gold. They were then cut and shocked, ready for that glorious time of year that all farmers awaited — threshing time.

While there were always at least eight bundle racks in each of the big runs, I managed to get by with four racks to haul bundles from the field to the machine, and two spike pitchers in the field to help load the wagons. Uncle Dave had a run of his own, but always finished in time to help me out. Mr. Schlichting and Fred could be counted on to be on hand, and Fred Benn took over the task of stacking my straw. It was the most disagreeable job of all, and brought extra pay to the man willing to go on the stack. Fred Benn would have felt slighted if I had asked anyone else to do it, and the only compensation he asked was that I help him out sometime.

He was a real neighbor, always ready to drop his own work for someone else. It was "Pa" Benn who was called on to stick a hog or beef at butchering time, Pa Benn who was troubled to help a neighbor get his cow out of the mud, and Pa Benn who was among the first to be summoned to every neighborhood tragedy. Why, hadn't he helped pull out a woman who had drowned herself in a stock tank on the very farm I was on, not many years before my father bought the forty?

Mrs. Benn was a typical robust farm wife, a hard worker and an excellent cook. I don't believe I ever saw her but that I was reminded how much she resembled Mrs. Eleanor Roosevelt, had that good lady been a farmer's wife instead of a president's. Mrs. Benn's yard was always full of chickens, ducks, geese, and turkeys; her garden plentiful with vegetables and berries; and her table lavish. I sometimes suspected that she wore the pants in the family.

It was only natural that for everyone in the neighborhood the threshing at the Benn farm should be the climax, the very spirit of the harvest scene itself. I shall never forget the last time I helped Mr. Benn thresh. The night before he was to have the threshers, Fred called me up to ask me to bring my team and rack.

I was up earlier than usual the next morning, milked the cows, finished the chores, and harnessed the horses before breakfast. By six-thirty my team and rack were clop-clopping over the hard gravel road. Other racks joined in the clamorous din, and their echoes roused the sleepy world to boisterous life. The schedule for the day began at seven.

Ebenezer Dodds, the owner of the threshing machine, was the top man and the boss. He had been on the job shortly after daybreak, oiling his machine and checking it thoroughly so that all would be in readiness by seven. There must not be a breakdown, once the bundles commenced feeding the hungry mouth of the machine. Nothing exasperated a threshing crew more than a breakdown, and the owner of the machine made every effort to eliminate this source of trouble. He ran the show and enforced the unwritten rules of sportsmanship; the first rack up to the machine in the morning was the first one to quit at night; racks were alternated on the belt side of the rig, and on windy days were interchanged on the dirty side.

The work of threshing was apportioned to each group of men. The older men hauled grain to the bins; the strong young men and older boys hauled bundles from the field and pitched them into the machine. Here was work that proved a man to his neighbors. It required a grueling amount of strength, stamina, and practice to load bundles so that the rack would appear square and high, and would not upset in the field when one side became top-heavy or when the rack was pulled over a ditch; these same sterling qualities were necessary in unloading the huge racks of bundles in order that both men on each side of the conveyor would finish about the same time to allow the next pair of racks to come up to the feeder together.

There was always keen competition in threshing as if it were as much a sport as baseball or football, a feeling of friendly rivalry in doing a task better than the other fellow. Every farmer prided himself on his team of horses. Spirited, well-matched horses that looked good on the road and pulled well in the field were prized possessions and subjects for many a discussion during brief moments of rest at the water can or under the shade trees after dinner — horses that would "giddap" and "whoa" without rein pressure as the bundle hauler moved down the windrow of shocked grain, pitching from the ground. A team that was trained to do this was invaluable in getting a rack loaded in record time. At threshing time the owner of a fine team bedecked the bridles and harnesses of his horses with rich ornamental trappings, consisting of bright-colored celluloid rings and brilliant red tassels.

The morning wore on. I could hear the old familiar sounds that fit the festive excitement of the harvest; the clatter of bundle racks, the hum of belt pulleys, the slashing of feeder knives, the roar of the tractor, the shouting of men to each other and to the horses, the sudden groaning of the separator when too many tough bundles were fed too quickly by the brawny bundle pitchers, and the steady rush of grain down the chute into the wagon boxes.

The morning was long and hot and dirty. The humming of the separator grew monotonous. The semicircular straw pile became higher and higher as the blower continued sweeping back and forth over the bright straw. At last when the sun beat down directly overhead, the machine stopped for dinner. The horses were unhitched, taken to the house yard, and watered out of the stock tank. While the horses drank, the men removed the first layers of sweat, chaff,

and dirt by scrubbing in the water tank. The teen-age boys engaged
in a sham battle by scooping up water in their cupped hands and dash-
ing it in the faces of their opponents; occasionally they became so
boisterous as to gang up on an adversary, pick him up bodily, and duck
him into the tank. After the horses had either finished drinking or
had been frightened back by the water fight, their owners led them
away and tied them with halters to the rear of their racks, where
special wooden feedboxes were attached in which each horse received
a gallon of oats and a forkful of hay.

At an outdoor washstand near the kitchen the men removed the
rest of the grime from their faces, necks, and hands. Here again each
man took his turn. He combed his hair hurriedly, seldom if ever
managing to locate the exact part in it, and took a quick look in a
cloudy mirror hung up under a tree for that purpose before going
into the dining room by way of the front porch.

Mrs. Benn judged the quality of her cooking by the amount of food
the harvesters ate, and by that infallible criterion was well satisfied.
Although every woman in the run tried to outdo the next one in
setting a lavish table for threshers, they all had to throw up their
hands in complete failure when they tried to vie with "Ma" Benn for
this honor. Her harvest table was replete with every kind of viand
that could come out of a farmwife's kitchen; fried chicken, mashed
potatoes and gravy, cabbage and banana salad, creamed peas and car-
rots, spiced Whitney apples and dill pickles, jams and jellies, coffee,
milk, and water, hot buns with fresh butter and honey, cocoanut
cream and one-crust apple pie, two kinds of cake, fruit salad, a bowl
of assorted fruits, and ice cream.

The men needed no help piling their plates high with food, although
Ma Benn stood by anxiously, lest the dizzily spinning wheel of food
around the table be stopped, and someone go hungry. Every time
there appeared a break in the edible parade, she stuck her red and
pudgy hand over the shoulders of the men with a replenished dish,
firmly believing that if she could cram the last mouthful of food down
the uncomfortable men it would be saved and not wasted. It was
incredible the quantity of food devoured and the speed with which
it was dispatched. Laughter and talking were general around the
table, but did not interfere with the eating.

Fritz was telling Merle Green about the new combine he and his
father were purchasing to combine their beans.

"Some of the farmers in the north run are using combines for their oats," Merle said, chawing a mouthful of chicken. "I don't think they will ever replace the threshing machine though, do you, Fred?"

"I dunno," the other replied, his fork paused in mid-air with a mound of potatoes stacked precariously on it, "but I wouldn't give a hang for the straw after it's combined!"

"You're right, there," agreed Merle. "The chaff, the best part of the straw, is lost in combining, and the straw you do get is full of cornhusks."

The younger men were eating at one end of the table by themselves and were carrying on their own conversation, mostly relating to the North Iowa Fair then in progress, and boasting of the prowess they would display at the shooting gallery or at the ball-throwing concession on Saturday night. Old Barney Sloan, the oldest man in the run, was listening to the boys make their plans as he shoveled the meat and potatoes into his mouth, his gray beard dripping with gravy.

"He! He!" he tittered, bringing a knifeful of peas to his wizened lips, "Benny here'll be taking his new girl Corie to the fair and will he do some spooning, come Saturday night!"

Several of the older men overhead this horseplay and guffawed. Benny, a lad of sixteen, flushed guiltily, which brought into a sharper relief on his cheeks the many brown freckles that were only slightly darker than his tanned complexion. His black hair was slicked down on both sides of his protruding forehead, with a small unruly bristle sticking straight up from the top of his head.

Ma Benn came to his rescue. "Land sakes! You'd think that boys were criminals to hear you talk. But believe me, I could tell a thing or two about you grown-up men that'd put you to shame. Many's the time I've seen you old men — and that don't excuse my old man — take a load of hogs to town, get soused, and bring a load of hogs back home."

It was the boys' turn to laugh now, and they made the most of it. Hal Jenkins, a stout, handsome, blond fellow, made a propitiatory speech, as he smacked his lips after drinking his cup of coffee, "Ma Benn, you make the best coffee in the county. What brand do you use?"

"Never use nothin' but Chocolate Cream," she beamed, brushing a wisp of brown hair back from her forehead. "The secret of makin' good coffee is to use an egg."

"Never heard of it," grunted Old Barney, sopping up his gravy with a wad of bread.

The weather was discussed, as were the oat yield and the danger of a war in Europe. Finally Eb Dodds, the boss of the outfit, turned to Fred Benn, and asked, "What are you going to do, Fred, make two straw piles, or put it all in one?"

"I hadn't planned on so much straw in the oats this year," Benn answered, scratching his red, bulbous nose. "I'd like to get it all in one stack, even if we have to move the machine and build on to the main stack after it's topped out."

Eb was a man of action and of few words. Now he leaned his long lean frame forward and with his customary "Yeah, it's a fittin' proposition," resumed eating.

Fred Benn was a small man and crouched beside Eb at the table like a bantam rooster, and with just as much grit. Mr. Benn had rented the farm he was on for nearly twenty years before he decided to buy it, and now with almost herculean effort was getting it paid for.

One by one the men got up from their chairs, rubbed their bellies, adjusted their belts to accommodate the unusual pressure against them, and staggered outside to rest for a while under the shade trees. Promptly at one o'clock the tractor started up and the machine was again in operation. Everyone was back at his job. The afternoon was very hot. Some of the zest and excitement of the morning was gone now. The excessive heat and toil were beginning to show on both the men and horses. The work continued, however, unabated, but with a lethargy that was absent during the fresh morning hours.

The straw stack had been lengthened, and by five o'clock in the afternoon, the two men in the stack were topping it out. Presently, Fred Benn waved his straw hat to the separator boss, indicating that he did not want any more straw on the stack, and the blower was turned to the end of the pile where the straw poured forth onto the ground. When Fred would get around to it, he would put weights on the stack to keep the wind from blowing the top off; then he would clean up around the sides and ends of the pile, hauling the loose straw into the barn in his rack.

Now he climbed down from the finished straw stack, removed his straw hat, and wiped the chaff and perspiration from his face and neck, as he proudly surveyed the finished stack. Farmers then valued their straw as highly as the oats themselves, if not more. It meant not only feed and bedding during the coming long months of winter, but protection for the stock as well, when they would seek refuge on its south side against the icy blasts from the northwest.

The first bundle racks were emptied and had started out of the yard toward their own respective homes. The men with the last loads were cleaning up the scattered bundles around the machine, when the first puffs of smoke were seen coming from the top of the great stack of straw.

"The straw stack's afire!" one of the men shouted.

Teams that were near the stack whinnied at the smell of the smoke, and veered away in fright. Men shouted wildly, and rushed madly to get their teams and wagons away. The tractor man jumped off the machine and threw the belt, putting the separator out of operation. He backed up to the threshing machine, and in his haste and excitement missed the tongue, and nearly smashed into the machine.

Great clouds of smoke were by now billowing into the sky. The women and children came screaming from the house. The black sky suddenly turned red as the fire burst free from the mountain of straw. The threshing machine was ablaze even as it was rushed away from the gigantic conflagration. The men did not attempt to put out the fire in the stack. All realized the futility of such an undertaking. They concentrated their attention on the machines and buildings nearby. The fire was soon extinguished on the separator, and everything else had been removed to safety.

The dry straw burned as if oil had been poured over it. The heat was so intense that it was impossible to remain near the blaze. No one knew what had caused the fire. Several theories were advanced. Perhaps it had been caused by a cigarette butt. Yet no one had seen anyone smoking near the stack. A more logical explanation was offered: a stone or a piece of steel might have been picked up with the scattered bundles while cleaning up around the machine and had gone through the separator, causing a spark which had ignited the straw.

Fred Benn watched the precious pile go up in smoke and flames, his tiny form pitifully insignificant against the giant conflagration. His face was tightly drawn like a person experiencing great physical pain, and his eyes continued to stare tragically, almost bitterly at the flames. The men came up to him, expressed their heartfelt feelings for their neighbor's great loss, and promised him at least one load of straw apiece. That was the way neighbors in the country did in times of misfortune. That was a part of their life.

After the last man in the run had his oats in his bin, Ebenezer Dodds held a "settling-up night," at which time the farmers who had not paid their threshing bill gave the owner of the machine a check for the amount due him. Ice cream and cake were served to the men and their families. This event was always eagerly awaited by young and old. Here the women of the neighborhood got together for the one time in the year, and became better acquainted, learned new ideas, and carried on the traditional feminine gossip party. The men smoked and drank beer, talked over events of the past and their plans for the next year, discussed new and better ways of farming, argued political issues, and left with a better understanding of their fellow farmers and their fellow human beings throughout the world.

I happened to be near Fred Benn when he gave Eb his check for threshing his oats. Eb wrinkled his nose, shoved the check back in Fred's trouser pocket, and said with a dismissive voice, "Forget it, 'taint a fair proposition, me takin' your money like that."

"But I still got the oats in the bin, Eb!" Fred insisted, holding the check out in his hand; but Eb walked away without taking it.

Today the combines harvest the small grain crops. In combining, there is no oat shocking nor bundle hauling. The grain is cut and threshed in the field in one operation; it requires the help of but two or three men. The work of harvesting the oats is greatly lessened and considerably shortened. The once familiar straw stacks with their valuable bedding material, as much a part of every farmstead as its silos, are no longer seen around the farmyards of Iowa in the fall and winter. Machines have taken the place of the horse, which is fast disappearing from the farming picture. Laborsaving combines have cut from the life of Iowa farmers a custom of cooperative neighborliness as real as the spirit of Christmas and Thanksgiving; and with the passing of the threshing machines — an old custom that was inconsistent with progress — an era of vital Iowa history passes away forever.

☆IX☆

The Feeding of Holsteins

Now THAT my small herd was being tested for production, there was a mounting interest for me in learning everything I could about dairying. I read every word of the *Holstein-Friesian World* from cover to cover; in fact, I was able to obtain copies of the breed publication for years back, which Mr. Schlichting had scrupulously saved. In this way I soon acquired a ready knowledge of the bloodlines of all the best herds in North America. I collected all the bulletins on feeding, breeding, and management that were obtainable from the different state colleges and read them avidly. I was more demanding than ever with questions put to my neighbor breeders, and from the cow tester I pried information concerning the herds he visited regularly once a month. All this information I carefully weighed in my own mind, and as carefully observed my own herd from day to day. Several ideas and theories of others were assiduously incorporated in my own methods of dairying; others were taken with a grain of salt; still others were entirely disregarded as new theories of my own were formed.

Edward Norris was the first cow tester at Arnewood. His work was to weigh each milking of each cow for the day he was at the farm. The samples of milk were then tested for butterfat percentage, and the amount of butterfat in the total amount of milk for the month was computed. At the end of the year one knew how much milk and fat each cow in his herd produced. There were usually about twenty-five dairy farmers in a county who were interested in the improvement of their herds and who would join such an association. The state colleges offered courses of instruction for men interested in learning to become cow testers for the different county associations. All records of production were turned into the state college office at the end of each year by the testers throughout the state; these records were forwarded to the United States Department of Agriculture to be used in computing bull indexes, the average production of dairy cows in the United States, and other valuable information. The tester kept records also of feed costs for each animal, in order to show the farmer which cows were his most profitable producers.

With each visit the cow tester suggested to the farmer ways in which the ration for the cows could be improved. Ideas were exchanged, and much benefit was derived. On several occasions Mr. Norris remarked over the very small amount of protein being fed to my cows. Dairy cows require certain amounts of protein to produce large quantities of milk.

"Your ration is very low in protein," he said. "The other dairymen in the association are feeding much more than you are."

Soybean and linseed oilmeals are the commonest sources of protein in concentrated form. I seldom fed more than half a pound a day to my best producers.

"I realize," I answered, "that my grain ration is very low in protein, but I have a much better source of protein in the hay that I am feeding."

I took Mr. Norris into the part of the barn where the bales of alfalfa were piled, and unfastened the wires around one of the bales. The slices of pea-green hay fell apart, revealing an abundance of leaves and fine stems.

"Here is the secret of high production in dairy cows," I said, picking up a handful of the soft alfalfa. "With hay like this, so rich in protein, my cows wouldn't need an ounce of oilmeal. Too often the quality of roughage in a cow's ration is overlooked, and cows are fed large amounts of concentrated proteins; this system of feeding shortens a cow's life and causes much udder trouble. Besides, hay is the cheapest source of protein. Just smell this hay."

"It smells just like a field of new-mown hay," he commented, holding a handful of it to his nose. "I suppose you're right about that. Your cows milk very well. We were taught to figure the amount of digestible protein from the grain ration and advise accordingly how much oilmeal to feed."

"The quality of the hay is vital to every dairyman," I replied, "and varies more than anything else he feeds. That's the reason I don't even try to grow my own hay any more. The weather here in Iowa makes hay-making a very difficult job. It's almost impossible to get hay up without a rain. I put land into corn that I would otherwise put into hay, and get much more from my corn than I would get from the hay. In that way I can buy the best hay that can be shipped in from the western states, where conditions are more favorable for hay-making."

"But is that a good soil-building practice," the tester interrupted, scraping some manure off his right shoe on the doorsill — "putting corn in year after year?"

"I don't worry about robbing the land. Since every acre on the farm is tillable, I never put corn on the same ground two years in succession. Then, too, every acre is heavily fertilized every year, and as I am a great believer in good pastures, there is always at least a third of the farm in pasture."

"I never realized there might be so much importance to hay and pastures," my genial friend said, after thinking the matter over for some time. "I've noticed that your cows almost wade in grass, while most other herds of cattle I see along the road graze on pastures that are always nipped to the ground."

"The biggest mistake most farmers make," I answered, "is when they overgraze a pasture. Grasses are richest in protein and organic salts early in the spring before they toughen and joint. Spring pastures are the best sources also for minerals and vitamins. A cow should be able to fill up within an hour so she can lie down to chew her cud. She eats upwards of a hundred pounds of grass in a day. Each cud weighs about four ounces and is chewed for about a minute, requiring her to spend about seven hours each day for this job alone. How'll she have time to do this if she has to spend the entire day picking over the pasture, and then not even getting filled up?"

"I appreciate your explaining this important subject to me," Ed Norris said, and, stepping out of the barn, took a cigarette from his pocket and lighted it. "I can show other dairymen now the importance of good pastures and hay."

The heifers grew and in time they freshened one by one. Snooks, too, came into the milking herd at last; but she was a great disappointment, giving scarcely enough milk for her own calf. Strange, I thought, how the laws of breeding work! Here was a heifer out of perhaps one of the greatest producers in the county, and sired by a bull that was proved for high production; yet she herself was a sorry animal.

Snooks became more and more of a problem in behavior. On one occasion she kicked the cow tester, causing him to walk with a limp for several months. Finally, but with great reluctance, I sold her.

I made up for the loss of this heifer by purchasing from Carnation Milk Farms, Seattle, Washington, a young female that I had painstakingly selected for a great foundation animal. I had begun to think about a breeding program. Most of my best animals were daughters of the sire, Pabst Sir Cascade Mignonette, the meritoriously proved son of Carnation Sensation. After much deliberation, I decided to hook up to the Carnation bloodlines, and in choosing the heifer from the West Coast I indulged in the first and only extravagance of buying in my herd. The cost of this one animal was $750, and that was a fairly good sum of money in the days just before the era of high prices during and following World War II.

This heifer's name was Carnation Heilo Perfection Beauty, and she carried the very best blood that the Carnation people had to offer. Beauty freshened with her first calf shortly after reaching Arnewood, and at once became a favorite. At first she did not know what flies were, there being few flies in the state of Washington, and Beauty stood still while the flies almost ate her up. She did not understand that her tail could serve a very useful purpose in the scattering of the tormentors. The little heifer simply bawled until I came to her and let her into the barn. In this way she soon became dependent on my waiting on her.

I had no illusions about the highly speculative game of breeding purebreds. One does not have to go far in the art of livestock breeding before he learns this one fact, and this alone makes every successful mating such a rich reward. Little Beauty was a living testimonial of this fact. In her royal veins flowed more than ten crosses to King Segis and to his son, King Segis 10th, the bulls that founded the Carnation bloodline.

Even the famous Carnation herd went through such a series of hardships that a less determined man than its founder, E. A. Stuart, could not have endured. First it was the Snoqualmie River, an enemy which attacked him for years every time he turned his back, an enemy that changed his methods of attack each time it struck, sneaking in where it was least expected and taking new strength from a hidden source to strike again. Then it was the job of clearing six hundred acres of the most impossible clutter conceivable. Originally the job was to have been done for $35 an acre; but when it was finished, after seven years of constant work with a crew of between fourteen and twenty men, it had cost nearly $200 an acre. Today there is no evidence of these difficulties at the Carnation Milk Farms. From a veritable city of gleaming white and green buildings on a pine-clad hill, the many green pastures with their white wooden fences spread away to the peacefully moving river in the distance. It has been called the "Home of Contented Cows," and no better description has ever been found for it. It is indeed a spot of exquisite, picturesque beauty, a place of quiet serenity, a pattern of harmony.

In founding this herd, Mr. Stuart had for his motive the highest one possible: that of breeding a herd of profitable producing cows so that farmers throughout the country could purchase bulls at a reasonable price to improve the producing ability of their own herds. This man stopped at nothing to achieve his goal, going so far as to pay $106,000 for a bull calf. This was the highest price ever paid for a Holstein. The bull's name was Carnation King Sylvia, and that memorable sale was held in Milwaukee, Wisconsin, on June 8, 1918. This bull, however, did not exert any lasting influence on the herd.

The bull that was to be the foundation of the Great Carnation herd

THE FEEDING OF HOLSTEINS

was already at the farm. He had been picked up with a small group of cows in a little herd in Idaho. The owner of the cows insisted that Mr. Stuart take the bull for nothing as long as he had purchased all of his cows. At first Mr. Stuart did not want the shaggy old bull, King Segis 10th, who was as crippled as he was ugly; but after much argument the bull was taken to the Carnation Farm, where he got a stall under the barn so that he could not be seen. The bull had been so cross that at one time his former owner had let him have a slug of buckshot just to show him where to draw the line. From this incident he received the name Old Buckshot. Alone and unwanted, Old Buckshot passed his few remaining days in the stall under the barn. After his death, one of his daughters, Segis Pietertje Prospect, became the first cow in the world to produce more than 37,000 pounds of milk in a year. When King Segis 10th's grandsons were mated to his granddaughters it was discovered that the more his blood was intensified the greater were the results. Old Buckshot proved to be one of the greatest bulls of all time.

The first cooperative artificial breeding association in Iowa was organized at Kanawha, about forty-five miles from Arnewood. Although I was out of the territory of the breeding ring, I was able to obtain a restricted contract to use the sires they had in service, which included three proved Carnation bulls, one of them the winner of an Iowa high-index sire award. This enabled me to follow through my plans of line-breeding to the Carnation bloodline.

Classification for type was another step in building a herd of choice dairy cows. Arnewood was one of the first herds in North Iowa to be classified. Professor F. W. Atkeson from the University of Kansas, one of the official inspectors for the Holstein-Friesian Association of America, made the ratings on my herd. All but two animals received "Very Good" ratings, and those two were classified "Good." These scores were arrived at from a type standpoint without any regard for production.

The first year that my herd was on test for production, it averaged 349 pounds of butterfat, a creditable showing; yet I was not satisfied. One of the cows produced only 250 pounds of fat, thus pulling the average down; so she was mercilessly sent to the market. With this one exception, I was unusually fortunate in selecting the foundation herd of purebreds.

I was not so fortunate, however, in making my first bull sale. A

Holstein breeder in the county purchased two bull calves from me at one time, and because he was a person of some property, the calves were sold with the understanding that he would pay for them within a very short time. In the meantime, the calves died, and he gave me a cow in payment for the two bull calves.

Having learned the dangers of Bangs disease, I always followed the precaution of testing every new member of the herd as soon as it came on the place. This cow was accordingly tested, and showed a positive reaction to the dread disease. No time was lost in sending her to the butchers.

"Mel, you must exercise the greatest caution against this thing," Mr. Schlichting had advised me. "Bangs strikes without warning. It has ruined hundreds of dairymen. It not only wipes out one or more crops of calves, but it cuts down the milk production severely. I had a neighbor some years ago who started in the purebred business. He borrowed money and bought several very good cows. He signed up with the government to have them tested for Bangs. Most of them reacted and had to be slaughtered, with an indemnity of fifty dollars a head paid to him. This was scarcely half, however, the original price of the animals. My friend was ruined and never ventured into the purebred game after that."

"Did he have to sell them?" I asked.

"Yes, after signing, he was forced to sell them. The test and slaughter method in eradicating Bangs will never be so satisfactory as it is in eradicating tuberculosis. You can send your entire herd to the block and buy in again, only to find that Bangs is still with you. It is wrong to sacrifice these animals in this way — animals that can never be replaced. There is a better plan, and eventually some drastic revisions will have to be made in the present law. These positive animals can be quarantined and saved for their offspring. The young herd should be vaccinated; and in time, as the older animals leave, the entire herd through vaccination will be immune to the disease."

At that time most of the states did not recognize calfhood vaccination, but today vaccination with Strain 19 is recognized by all states as an important part of the control of brucellosis, or Bang's disease.

Another matter that early prompted my special attention was that of feeding minerals. Salesmen who peddled high-priced minerals from farm to farm were always a nuisance. Advertisements stressing the need for these minerals and the dire consequences resulting from not feeding them were so ballyhooed everywhere, in the papers, over the radio, and on roadside signs that I bought some and fed them to the cows. The animals did not care for them. I was determined to investigate the matter. The leading herds in the country, and the experimental station of our own state college, all had the same experiences and concluded that common salt and steamed bone-meal were the only additional minerals necessary to feed, with the possible exception of iodine in regions where that trace mineral has been drained from the land.

Since then my own theory has been that the best way to feed minerals to livestock is to feed them back into the soil from which they have been drained, and they will get back into the forage in the form and degree best suited to the needs of farm animals.

This, as well as many other theories connected with the intricate details of dairy cattle breeding, was learned only after years of study and observation. At that early period when I was forming my herd, I was only beginning to become curious about these things, as I had always been about the phenomena of nature.

There were so many things that demanded my attention. So many things were going on in the world about me. The years were slipping by faster and faster. Actually it had been three autumns ago that I had taken over the farm. The seasons still held their charm, their mystery. And so 1940 eased into the full color of fall. The wild grape vines were heavy with purple clusters on the fence along the road; the corn shucks opened on the graying stalks of corn, revealing their golden shafts of grain, and the sumac east of the house turned brilliant red. I worked those days beneath smoky Indian summer skies, and slept peacefully at night, awakened sometimes by the honking of the flocks of wild geese and ducks in flight.

Testing the Arnewood Herd

By 1941 THE war in Europe had changed many things, even on an Iowa farm. The Selective Training and Service Act was mobilizing this nation's manpower, and the effects of the rationing of certain food items were already being felt. The shortage of labor on the farms and the demand for increased production placed the American farmer in a strained position. When Pearl Harbor was attacked in December, and the United States entered the war, the farmers' problems were further increased.

The year also brought changes to my family. In November my father was killed in an auto accident. My brother Oliver enlisted in the Army Air Corps and was sent to India. As for myself, I would have escaped the draft because of occupational deferment for a while at least, but I should have never felt right about that. I was determined to get it over with as soon as possible. I passed my preliminary examination in the county, and had resigned myself to the inevitable: dispersal of the herd and entering the service. But, after a rigid examination at Camp Dodge, I was not accepted for military service. And so I returned to Arnewood.

Now that I had a fine foundation herd assembled, I began working in earnest to put it on top. Early in 1942 the first modest advertisement from Arnewood appeared in the *Iowa Holstein Herald*, offering for sale a bull calf from the Princess cow, that had just finished a record of 405 pounds of fat. The calf was sold within a few days, and inquiries concerning bull calves began pouring in. The small quarter-page advertisement grew until finally the Arnewood herd advertisement received a full page on the back front cover of the state Holstein magazine.

The weather was ideal that summer, and the pastures were excellent. The cows milked heavily throughout both the spring and the summer months, promising some rather fine records. During the hottest parts of the day the cows were stanchioned in the barn and fed additional hay. The doors and windows of the stable were darkened with burlap sacks to keep the interior as cool as possible and to discourage flies from coming in. Flies do not cause the decline in milk flow during the summer months that they are generally accused of. The main reasons for a summer slump in production are hot weather and a reduction in good quality feed.

Princess was leading the cows in my herd month after month in production — Princess, the big white cow that had so nearly been sent to the block as a two-year-old heifer because she had been a kicker. She would far surpass her previous 400-pound record, and a 400-pound butterfat record on twice-a-day milking under ordinary farm conditions is considered a very good one. Of a total of 536 cows tested in Cerro Gordo County during 1942, only 22 produced more than 400 pounds of fat. These figures will illustrate the remarkable showing made by the Arnewood herd for that year. The average butterfat production for the entire herd was 484 pounds. This was the highest producing herd in Cerro Gordo County for the year; the second high herd produced an average of 397 pounds. Princess' record of 637 pounds fat for the year made her the highest producing cow in the county, and the only one to make over 600 pounds of fat.

Mr. Schlichting and Fred came down one morning shortly after the production lists were announced in the Mason City *Globe-Gazette*. Henry grinned as he said, "I see by the paper that you beat us this year."

"I'm happy I did," I replied, "and though I hate to admit it, I consider that quite an accomplishment."

"Well," Fred drawled, "I suppose we'll have to concede you got the edge on us, but I still say we have just as good cows. You took better care of yours than we did, that's all. You could probably get good records out of scrubs."

"You'll have to admit, though, just the same," I countered, "that I picked the good ones when I bought them."

"Yes," Henry agreed, stroking his chin with his hand, "you did get some of our very best ones. What did Maggie finish with?"

"Maggie had 591 pounds of fat, and was second on the list of high producers," I answered. "In addition, there were four other cows in my herd that made over 500 pounds fat."

"A remarkable showing, Mel," Mr. Schlichting concluded, "considering the size of your herd. Come, show us Beauty's bull calf. We might like to buy him."

After this initial success, the herd was placed on Herd Improvement Registry Test, a more rigid type of supervisory test than that of the Cow Testing Association. This new method of testing was in charge of the Superintendent of Advanced Registry of the Holstein-Friesian Association of America, and under the supervision of the state colleges. Just as in the C.T.A. work, the Herd Improvement Registry has for its purpose the obtaining of records on every cow in the owner's herd year after year. This form of testing has always been my choice because I believe it does the most good for the improvement of the breed. Advanced Registry testing, a third type of testing, will always have its place in the necessary part of breed promotion with its glamorizing records made on the selected individuals of a herd, with the main purpose of securing large records on the best cows of the breed; but it can never take the place of the Herd Test where each cow is tested every year so that her entire life's production is officially recorded. It often happens that even a poor cow can make one large record, but this is no indication that she can do it year after year; and in the end the important thing in building a herd of dairy cows is to obtain individuals that will not only produce profitably year after year, but will transmit this ability to their daughters and granddaughters.

The cows at Arnewood were allowed to take their time. They were never hurried in and out of the stable as are so many cows. This carefulness paid off several times. Cows handled in this way often obey their caretakers at a word from them, thus saving the farmer many steps. When Lily felt like taking the wrong stanchion, I had only to say "Lily" and she remembered her place. Many falls on the slippery cement floor can be prevented in this way, and valuable animals saved from possible serious injury.

The maternal instinct of a dairy cow is to give milk to her calf. If a dairyman would learn to gain his cow's affection, he, instead of her calf, could become the cow's center of devotion, and she would want to give her milk to her master. When dairymen realize this primal law of nature, they will have learned the fundamental key to all dairy success.

The next year was to see the herd do even better, with an average of 494 pounds fat, and Princess repeated her performance as the highest producing cow in the county! The herd had now achieved recognition far beyond any I had ever dreamed of.

With each success, however, there was always a price to pay. Perhaps that explained why each reward became so dear to me. During the summer of 1942 it was extremely difficult to get help with the rush work on the farm. Because of the war there were few young men left in the neighborhood. I did not notice the labor shortage so much on my own farm, since I had always done most of my own work anyway; but on the larger farms it was different. Uncle Dave was constantly pressed for additional help. Always a big, strong man, my uncle had never complained about getting his work done. His threshing run had always finished ahead of any other run; his hay had always been the first to be put into the barn; his corn had always been cribbed before any other farmer had finished picking.

It was while we were stacking soybeans that my uncle suddenly took ill. I had never known him to be off duty a day in his life, and I felt very much depressed that Sunday morning as I visited him in his room. He was very pale and extremely weak, yet attempted to smile when I entered.

"Aren't I the good one, getting sick just in the middle of the work?" he said whimsically.

"You just worked at it a little too hard," I returned lightly, seating myself on a chair near his bedside, "and need a few days' rest. Don't worry about the work. We'll see that it gets done, and in a few days you'll be as good as new."

"Don't youse go working too hard," he fretted. "The beans can stay out in the field for a spell, and those cows of yourn keep you plenty busy t'home."

"Well, promise me that you'll call if there is anything you want."

"I will," my uncle agreed. "How's Beauty?"

He was always concerned about this one heifer because I had paid such a large price for her, and because she was perhaps the most affectionate animal in the herd.

"I keep her in the barn most of the time, and Mother says she bawls for me all the time I'm away from the farm."

"You've gone and spoilt her, Melvin, that's what you've done," he said laughingly.

"I've brought you some of the apples from the tree at home. It's loaded, and there isn't a worm in any of them."

"They're nice apples," he said, proudly fondling one of them in his big hand. "They should keep a long time stored in the cellar."

"I want you to hurry up and get better so you'll be able to help me pick the apples this fall," I humored, slouching in my chair and crossing my legs.

But Uncle Dave did not get better. He was taken to the hospital the next day for an emergency operation, from which he never regained consciousness. The doctor said that my uncle had been worse off than any of us had realized, but that he had concealed his pain. By the time his condition was realized and he was taken to the hospital, it was too late. My uncle died on Tuesday, less than a year after my own father's untimely death, and I lost with him a man who was almost a father to me. I was shocked by this overwhelming loss. Like my own father's death, my uncle's was sudden and unexpected, and in my life there is a void left by his passing that can never be filled.

* XI *

I Lose My Herd

ONE AFTERNOON in August a big dark-colored Buick drove into the yard. I was mowing weeds with a scythe west of the house, and instantly recognized the car as one belonging to Hugh Shepard. I hung the blade in the crotch of a tree, grabbed from a tree branch the shirt that I had discarded in the heat of work, slung it over my shoulder, and walked toward the car. Mr. Shepard was one of the county's outstanding lawyers and had handled the affairs of the estate that owned the place I was renting. He had stopped at the farm but once or twice before during the several years I had been operating the forty. Whenever I had wanted some very necessary repair work done about the place, I had called upon him at his office in Mason City. I had done the same thing once every year when the rent was due. Mr. Shepard had always acted in the best interests of both landlord and tenant.

I was not at all surprised, however, at the purpose of his latest visit. He had mentioned on several different occasions during my visits at his office that the farm would some day be sold, and that he would like to help me get it.

"It seems," he now announced in his usual deliberate, booming tone of voice, "that the heirs are now ready to liquidate their farms in this part of the county, and I have been advised to sell yours along with the rest."

"What are they asking for it?" I asked, putting one foot on the running board of the Buick.

"One hundred and fifty dollars an acre," he replied in the same dry and powerful voice.

"I have given the matter a great deal of thought," I said, "and have decided to offer them $125 per acre. In fact, I have discussed this with some of my neighbors and they agreed that I would be foolish to pay any more than that amount, considering the condition the buildings are in. The land itself is excellent, but my herd has been built to such a point now that it is a disgrace to house them in such a stable. You know yourself what a new barn would cost."

"I quite agree with you there, Mr. Scholl; but land values are rising by leaps and bounds, and I believe that in a short time you'll find this place cannot be had even for $150 an acre. I have always been amazed at your progress with your cattle. It is hard to believe that here on this inconspicuous farm is assembled the finest herd of blooded cattle to be found in this part of the state; and yet on many of the farms with the finest sets of dairy buildings one finds only mediocre cattle."

"I have often wished," I commented, "that I had a fine barn for my cows. And yet I've always contended that a barn without good cattle is only a liability. Get the herd first and let it build the barn. The same is true with a farm itself. I suppose this farm is worth $150 an acre as long as the soil itself is so rich. The produce from this rich soil can in time furnish the money to build. So many farms have fine sets of buildings, but the land is so poor and run-down that it cannot maintain its buildings. I feel, nevertheless, that the heirs in this case should accept my offer for this farm as a very good one. I question very much if they'll get the price they are asking for it, and they should give me some consideration in this case. When my father bought this farm he spent several thousands of dollars in clearing the place. There were so many rocks and stumps in the fields that they had never been broken up before for cultivation. The field to the south was nothing more than a boggy slough until he tiled it. The fences were practically worthless. He put in hog-tight fences around the entire forty acres. The place went back to the estate with but a little more than two thousand dollars against it. Had my father put the same money in paying off the loan that he invested in improvements in the farm, the place today would be clear of debt. Besides that, I have paid good rent for many years, and have asked very little. In fact, most of the small repairs on the fences, buildings, and well came out of my own pocketbook, as you well know. In view of this, I will not give them a cent more than $125 an acre."

While I was talking, Mr. Shepard had reached over on the seat beside him to remove some papers from a worn brief case initialed with the gold letters: "H.H.S." From a case in his pocket he took a pair of dark-rimmed glasses and put them on beneath his dark and shaggy eyebrows. He jotted down some notes on the paper, and I noticed that his double chin was more pronounced as his lowered head moved back and forth with the movement of his pen. The mole on his left cheek followed the motion of the great head like some living thing.

"I shall write to them at once, stating exactly your terms," the stentorian-voiced Mr. Shepard promised, "and you can rest assured that I will do all in my power to help you. I have always given first consideration to the tenants on the farms I handle, and in this case I have a personal interest. I have realized the handicaps you were up against and the promptness with which you have met your obligations. Perhaps they'll see your point of view and accept your offer. We shall certainly hope they will. But," he added carefully, "if the farm should be sold away from you, I still want to help you. If you'll come to my office soon, I'll drive you out to my own farm west of town. I want you to see it. Its location is ideal for your purpose, and I should be very happy to get you on it. In fact, I should be very much interested in going into partnership with you if you feel you want to expand. I am convinced that you know your business with dairy cattle, and it would be a fine investment for me as well as a hobby."

"Thank you very much, Mr. Shepard, for your very fine cooperation with me in the past and your deep consideration and confidence in me now; but there can never be another Arnewood. If this farm is sold, the herd goes with it. I want to buy this place. It's the only place I want for my own herd, but I will not give more for it than I think it's worth."

"I hope you know what you're doing," my friend said as he started his car in preparation to leave, "but don't be too surprised if the farm is sold. There are parties that have been interested. I am not at liberty to say more; but for myself I want to see you get it. I shall do what I can."

A week or two later I received a letter from Mr. Shepard's office advising that the estate had decided that they still wanted the price they had been asking, but that if they were not able to get it, they would reconsider my offer. Different parties came to the farm during the remainder of the summer to look at it. They all shook their heads before leaving, convinced that by the time they had purchased the farm and made the necessary repairs to the buildings that had to be made, the price per acre would be too high. One cannot invest as heavily in buildings on a small farm as one can on a large farm where the cost over two or three hundred acres is materially lessened.

Came October. According to law a landlord must serve notice before the first day in November to his tenant concerning his intentions for the ensuing year, and vice versa. I had about convinced myself that the farm was not going to be sold when I received a registered letter from Mr. Shepard's office on October 31, advising me the farm had been sold to Ebenezer Dodds, the boss of the threshing run in our neighborhood. I was indeed surprised to learn that this particular man had purchased the farm without so much as looking it over. Mr. Shepard suggested that I contact Mr. Dodds immediately if I wished to rent the forty the next year.

I drove over to Eb Dodd's farm that very afternoon. Eb walked out to the car as soon as I drove into the yard. He was puffing away on his pipe. "Howdy, Mel, what's on your mind?"

"I received notice this morning from Mr. Shepard that you bought the farm I am renting," I began, opening the car door and sliding my legs out.

"Yes, the heirs of the estate stopped in here some time ago, and almost begged me to take the place off their hands. They have been

wanting to sell badly for a long time. I didn't like the proposition —,"
Eb filled his pipe with new tobacco, leaving his pet expression un-
finished.

"I would like to rent the forty for next year if I may," I said.

"I'm sorry, Mel, but one of the boys had intended moving on next
spring," he replied, almost before I had finished. "But don't be in any
hurry to move. You don't have to leave by March first. My boy probably won't get moved over till the weather breaks up. That will give
you plenty of time to find another place, or have a sale. Those cattle
of yours will bring a fine price. Everything is high right now. Fine
time to sell out."

"I am not interested in the price they will bring at a sale," I replied,
somewhat nettled by his attitude. "It is rather late in the season to
find another farm. The best ones are already gone. I suppose I should
have bought the place."

"But there are other ways to look at it, my son," Eb said, not unkindly, as he took a long puff on his pipe. "You would have had a
hard time even after you bought the farm to fix it up the way we'll
be able to fix it up."

"I have always had a hard time getting what I wanted," I returned,
finding it difficult to conceal the bitterness I felt, "but I have always
got it. The buildings would have come in time, too; perhaps not so
quickly as you could have them. We have lived there for a good many
years as they are, and would have been satisfied that way until we
could afford better ones."

"But, Mel," Eb Dodds countered, quick to notice the pique in my
words, "you can get a good job in the city where you don't have to
milk cows for a living."

"I'm very sorry you find it impossible to rent the forty to me for
another year. I don't believe I would want to work in the city even
if I have to sell my cows. Anyway," I added, pulling my legs back
into the car and shutting the door, "we'll be out as soon after March
first as we can, and thanks for giving us the extra time."

"Nothing at all. Don't even mention it," Eb said dismissively, gesturing with his pipe, and as I started driving out of the yard, he
called after me, "If you folks need any help for the sale, don't be
afraid to call on us."

In February of 1944, the *Holstein-Friesian World* carried a full-
page advertisement announcing the dispersal of my herd, and, during

the same month, this smaller notice appeared in the *Iowa Holstein Herald*:

A Farewell Message from Arnewood

Only because the farm has been sold, and I find it impossible to give this fine little herd the continued care it deserves, have I consented to this dispersal. My one earnest hope is that each one of my favorites finds a home where she will be cared for as devotedly as she was cared for here at Arnewood, and where she will bring as much pride and satisfaction as she brought me. I shall continue to watch their further promising development in the herds where they are destined to go; and to my many Holstein-Breeder friends I wish to say that I am not quitting the Holstein cow. In the future work that I have chosen I shall continue my deep interest in and strive toward the further advancement and glory of the breed. In the February 5th issue of the *World* will be a pictorial display of the stars of the sale, and as most Iowans are already acquainted with my herd, I shall let the cows speak for themselves on Thursday, February 24. . . .

The day of the sale will always bring back a confusion of memories to me. I had worked so hard getting the animals ready as well as lining up the machinery and the countless other articles to be sold that I was not only tired but also bewildered and dazed. The day itself was fine for the occasion, and there were cars from all parts of the state, and one even from Oklahoma.

The cows were sold and were scattered to all parts of the state. I was confused, and in my confusion I wondered if I had made a mistake in selling them. I certainly had not wanted to. But something — was it Providence? — had taken a hand in the matter, and I was powerless to do anything; it was as though there was something yet unaccomplished and I could do it in no other way.

Arnewood Amy was the last animal to leave the farm. A sickening feeling choked me as she left. The last vestige of Arnewood went with her. The soul of the place was gone. Arnewood was no more. I could not look upon it again. Only memories now — and the dormant apple tree in the garden.

Part Three

The Maytag Dairy Farms

✫ XII ✫

An Important Decision

Now I was to face one of the gravest crises in my life, with the entire course of future events depending on the decision I should make. I had owned several great cows, animals that would be a credit to any herd in the country; and yet I had not discovered that one cow I was searching for, the one every cowman hopes to find, the one which will make a 1,000-pound fat record for him — in a word, the cow that would embody all the fine qualities Cutie had possessed in fullest measure. Perhaps I was searching in vain.

Then, too, there were many questions in my mind still unanswered. Being a person who desires to probe the innermost secrets of nature, I could not be satisfied until I had conquered those mysteries. I was only beginning to understand the complexities of genetic principles that govern the success or failure of breeding dairy cattle. I was filled with awe and bewilderment at the responsibility of the man who dared to tamper with the creation of something beautiful — with life itself. To plan a mating with two animals, knowing each one's genetic make-up, and then to wait for the result of such a mating, visioning before-hand what that calf will be — such a task seemed almost a partnership with God! I knew that inherited traits are determined by the join-ing of the sperm and the egg, each of which contributes half of the genetic make-up of the offspring. But by the division of cells, the number of these carriers of traits is split in half, leaving the embryo with the traits inherited from both sire and dam. This distribution, determined entirely by chance, explains why even full brothers and sisters are often different, and in some cases may be direct opposites. A concentration of desirable chromosomes, to the exclusion of all others, is necessary, then, in obtaining animals with the desirable traits, which in dairy cattle are type, production, good udders, long life, strong constitution, and so on. How to breed homozygous animals that possess the desired traits so purely that the results of mating can be anticipated with fair uniformity requires careful study and obser-vation in a herd where such a breeding program has been carried on.

There were many important basic facts concerning feeds, disease, and management that I was determined to learn. I had long ago nar-rowed my field of decision down to three herds in America that could afford me the opportunity of achieving what I was looking for. Those herds were Carnation Milk Farms, Seattle, Washington; Pabst Farms, Oconomowoc, Wisconsin; and Maytag Dairy Farms, Newton, Iowa.

I needed time to think. I was tired both in mind and in body after losing so much I had loved. I needed a rest, a vacation. I had never had one, and I longed to make a tour of Iowa, the land I loved so well. Circumstances beckoned me to the perfect atmosphere for quiet rest-fulness and deep reflection, amid the scenic grandeur of northeast Iowa, a region rich in historic features and Indian lore, a country famed for its geological phenomena. The ruggedness of the terrain, so different from the level plains I had grown up with, gave me the complete change I needed.

Mr. and Mrs. Paul Behn, breeders of registered Holsteins in Franklin County, had just purchased a 320-acre farm between Decorah and Postville in Winneshiek County. They asked me to spend several weeks with them in their new home, and to help them get established. I readily accepted their invitation. Two of the females from my herd, Beauty and Bessie, had been added to Mr. Behn's good herd, and a third, Lily, had been purchased by Mr. Behn's new neighbor, Fennimore Ambrose.

Paul and Alice Behn had encountered most of the trials met with by young couples getting started in the purebred business, but they were advancing through sheer hard work and a genuine love for their Holsteins. As tenants, they had struggled alone through the war years on a large farm. Now at last they had succeeded in procuring a farm of their own in a region where dairying was predominant.

This forthcoming visit with them would give me the chance of seeing a place I had long yearned to see, the old home in Buck Creek where my mother was born. She had not seen the place for thirty-five years, and longed to go there again. I promised her that she would see it.

I wanted my first view of the Mississippi to be from Pike's Peak at McGregor, so we turned off right going into McGregor on a graveled road at a sign pointing to the elevation, named after the famous explorer, Zebulon Pike, who, in 1805, suggested it as a possible site for a fort. After winding around for about two miles in the Model A that I had acquired from Judy when she went into defense work, without any sense as to the elevation we were climbing, we were on top of the bluffs overlooking the Mississippi. Abandoning the car, we walked over to the magnificent promontory that juts out into the river, some four hundred feet below. I stood breathless at the most beautiful picture I had ever seen. Far below was the river, rushing madly in the center, while far away and back of many tree-dotted islands the water remained still, splashed with many varieties of plant life. Across the river was Prairie du Chien, located at the confluence of the Wisconsin and Mississippi rivers, on a wide, magnificent plain surrounded by thousands of verdant cedar trees. As I looked down and away to the south, I saw a train approaching the bridge to cross the Wisconsin River to Prairie du Chien. Fascinated, I watched the toylike train, and I tried to number the freight cars. After I had counted one hundred, I lost track; but there were many more than that — so many in fact that the engine was already rolling over the plain into Prairie du Chien while the string of cars stretched the length of the bridge across the river, and still part of the train had not yet reached the bridge. I could vision what this place meant in the vanished period when the Red Man's travels were reckoned by foot trail and by canoe. Why, actually, I thought, a rendezvous here at Prairie du Chien, where a water route opened to the Great Lakes and the St. Lawrence, to the pine forests of the North, to the headwaters of both the Ohio and the Missouri, and thence to the Gulf of Mexico, meant access to half a continent!

The faint, faraway whistle of the train intruded on my reveries, bringing me once more back to the world of realities. A purple martin, never seen at Arnewood, flew into the boughs of a maple tree a short distance to our right. Mother, standing beside me, continued to look out over the river and valley below, her hand raised over her eyes to shade them from the glare of the morning sun. There was just enough wind blowing over the tableland to billow out my mother's pink and gray flowered skirt. My eyes, too, turned again to the illimitable valley.

"It is hard for most people to realize the importance of this land to agriculture and to the very life of our country," I said seriously.

"What do you mean?" Mother asked, dropping her hand from her forehead and turning to me.

"Going way back into the histories of ancient civilizations it is evident that the rise or fall of those empires followed either the progress or decline of agriculture. The Nile Basin, comprising 10,000 square miles of the most fertile land on the Eastern Continent, is a shining example of what the ancients thought of the value of rich, fertile lands. To gain control of this basin, every world power engaged in bitter warfare and risked everything. Yet here in the Mississippi Valley we have an area of 200,000 square miles, twenty times the area of the Nile Basin, of grade A land, an empire so great that no other on earth can be compared to it either in size or in fertility."

"Then we should be thankful for that," Mother said softly.

"To be thankful for it is not enough," I returned. "It is our solemn duty to make it respond to the needs of our people and to conserve it for future generations."

"But aren't we doing just that?" my listener questioned. "This rich land can never be destroyed."

"Oh, but it can!" I corrected. "Our record in the past has been one of prodigality. We have wasted this fertility, and by improper methods of crop rotation have caused this precious soil to be eroded and swept downstream to clog our rivers and make floods more disastrous."

We turned away. The trail with its precipitous descent into the canyon to the Pictured Rocks was most inviting. The trail, zig-zagging down around the rocks for hundreds of feet, was steep and treacherous, and required considerable physical exertion. Sometimes we stopped to get our breath, and to admire the flowers that seemed at times almost to cling to the rocks — the crocus, the jack-in-the-pulpit, and the purple heart-leaved violet. The path became darker as trees and bluffs excluded the sunlight; the great rock cliffs were murky and cavernous, their surfaces green and slippery with lichen. Ferns of all varieties grew in abundance in the sandstone crevices. All at once we came to the colored sands. Against the bluffs we could see only traces of the fantastic shapes and designs formed by the painted sands. Trees had long since grown to such heights as partly to obscure the beauty that had once been so common there. Before the war, the park had employed men to scale the bluffs and keep the moss rubbed off the surfaces so the beauty of the rocks could be visible to the countless persons willing to make the sporting adventure into the canyon.

Although my mother had spent her early life in this region, she had never seen the Pictured Rocks before. She loved rock formations and brilliant colors of sands nearly as well as she loved flowers.

"I never dreamed anything so beautiful was here all the time," she exclaimed, almost out of breath. "But I don't think I should ever be able to climb down here again."

"I feel the same way," I said, wiping my brow with the back of my hand. "Come, take my arm; let's start up again."

Our automobile trek now took us away from the river, back through Garnavillo, and on to Buck Creek Valley. A touch of sublimity pervaded the air on that April morning as we entered the valley. I felt a sense of trespassing into the past, and a heady dizziness with the sheer beauty of the place. I was like an excited schoolboy exploring some land of fairy tale experience. There was a stillness about the valley that strangely enough could not be broken even by the soft singing of the first birds of spring or the whispers of the warm, scented breezes, sighing through the pine trees. These musical sounds seemed only to accentuate the silence of the place. The road was narrow and winding, like some old path through a primeval forest. It might have been there always. Above rose the pine-clad hills. To the right were the small, rich farms of the inhabitants of the valley; farther away the coy Buck Creek danced and tripped in the shadows of the foothills that rose again to their lofty green summits. In this quaint, picturesque setting I imagined I was in some Old World atmosphere.

Mother knew every trail, every landmark. As we passed one farm, she remarked reminiscently, "Old Biederman lived there when I was a girl."

We drove on, eager to reach our destination.

"Jake Biederman lived at the next place," she continued, her enthusiasm mounting, and the color rising to her cheeks. "He was one of the boys. Joe Biederman's farm was just beyond Jake's. Each one of them owned his own farm. All our neighbors owned their own farms then, and took good care of the rich bottom land. Harters lived down the road, and were our closest neighbors."

"Then we are getting near your old home?" I ventured.

"Yes," my mother answered, then added with a sigh, "I wonder if it has changed?"

The road continued to wind around the base of the hills, until we came to an apple orchard on our left. There were not many trees left in it, and those were old and twisted.

"I can remember when my father set out this orchard," my mother said. "That was just a few years before he sold the farm and moved to Guttenberg. The boys didn't care to stay on the farm because they could get better paying jobs in Dubuque without all the work of keeping up the farm as their father had done."

"Your old farm must start here," I hazarded a guess.

"Yes, over there to the right of the road, as far as the hills, stretched Father's hayfields, without a single weed in them. He made us children pull them out before they went to seed."

There was no sign of the hayfield now. In fact, a veritable forest of willows had grown up on the land, and it was evident by the size of some of the trees that the farm had not been cultivated for a score of years.

"The buildings must be just ahead," Mother said wistfully. "There should be a gate and a driveway on this side of the bridge."

AIRVIEW OF MAYTAG DAIRY FARM AT NEWTON

ELMER H. MAYTAG, *left*   MELVIN M. CAMPBELL, *right*

M. M. Campbell Home   Cheese and Milk Plant   Main Barn — south wing is Test Cow Barn   Calf Barn   Heifer Barn

Maytag Show Herd at International Livestock Exposition in Chicago

But as we came to the bridge, we could not see the gate leading to the buildings. Nor could we see either the house or the barn.

"They are back from the road behind that grove," Mother informed me. "But where is the road leading to them?"

We parked the car and got out. An old man was fishing from the bridge. I walked up to him and asked, "Doesn't anyone live here any more?"

"I reckon not, son," he drawled, removing a pipe from his mouth. "The folks useter live 'ere done sold out quite a spell ago. Moved ter town, I guess. Got tired clearin' the place aft'r ev'ry flood."

"Do you live around here, sir?" I asked politely.

The old man motioned up the road with his pipe, "Yah, I done bought me a little place catty-cornered of old Hank's up the road a pace. Kinda hankered fer a little peace 'n quiet in me old days, but my Mari'd kick the bucket if she couldn't raise the roof of'n the house. My Mari' —"

"My mother was born here," I said, concealing my impatience, "and we'd like to get up to the house."

"Ya don't say," my new acquaintance replied, spitting sharply. "Well, if'n youse have a mind t'see th' place — mind ya, I'll not be saying it's elegant as 'twas once upon a time — youse'll hav t' walk. Cain't get up there with the jitney. Crawl under the fence and cross the crick over yonder on them stones. Shore ya don't want t' turn back? Now, my Mari' —"

"Thank you, sir, but we'll be wanting to see the place," I interrupted. "We'll be leaving you alone now so we don't scare the fish."

"Oh, that's funny!" the old man exclaimed, clapping his pipe across his skinny knee, and laughing until there were tears in his eyes. "They ain't no fish in this crick!"

"Then why are you fishing?" I asked curiously.

"I jedge you hain't married, son!" he roared with laughter.

We left the fellow, still holding his sides to keep them from splitting, and took the direction he had pointed out, crossing the stream by stepping from one stone to another at a place where the water was shallow. Around the bend we saw the old barn and the house.

"There hasn't been a board touched since my father was here," Mother said sadly. "It used to be so lovely."

The door that led into the vegetable cave in the hillside was partly ajar. I pushed it open cautiously. It was dark and musty inside, and

I recoiled involuntarily. The thought of seeing a rattlesnake somewhere in the darkness was too real to escape. I went to the old mill
that had been converted into a barn. The stable beneath had filled up
with dirt and debris almost to the ceiling. The place was engulfed by
gnarled trees and vines. Unrestrained nature had made deep inroads
over a period of many years.

The house was boarded up and locked. The summer kitchen was
still there, as were the smokehouse and the hog house beyond, but they
were reposing in different stages of dilapidation. Gone were the neatly
grazed pastures on the near side of the dam where the lambs once
frisked in the sunshine; gone the potato patches and cornfields, the
lawn and the garden. In their place an inconceivable mass of wild vege-
tation had grown up, like some demon striving mercilessly to devour
all human workmanship. We turned and walked away.

Rose Harbor Holstein Farm was the new farm that Paul Behn had
purchased south of Decorah. It lay a mile long with the buildings in
the southeast corner. It had been the "Old Beard" estate in former
times, and most of the neighbors could still remember when it had
been the "show place" of Winneshiek County, when many persons
from Decorah and the surrounding towns had driven out on Sundays
and holidays in their bright surreys with smart driving horses just to
see the grand house and court.

Old Benjamin Beard was one of the earliest settlers in the county,
coming there in 1851. He purchased several sections of land from
the government for fifty cents an acre. He became one of the three
richest men in the county — one of only three men who had to pay
the enormous sum of twenty dollars in taxes.

His son, William Beard, improved the vast estate, building a
twelve-room mansion. Then, out of native lumber, much of it hand-
hewn, he erected two large barns, one for cattle, the other for the
many horses required to work the large estate. Other buildings included a corncrib and a granary, the latter still standing in its original
location. The farm had its own blacksmith shop. Many log cabins
were built to house the laborers that worked in the fields. These
people were newcomers from the Scandinavian countries.

By the time Paul Behn purchased the farm, a large wing of the
house had been dismantled, and the ornamental cornices and trim-
mings torn away. The white picket fence with its rare designing no
longer enclosed the once beautiful lawns, and the green rose espaliers

were rotted away. Fragments of the cement flower boxes that were built on the greensward were still visible. The house itself still displayed much of its former splendor. The large windows gave the huge rooms brilliant lighting effects — rooms richly adorned with beautifully grained and hand-carved walnut woodwork. A winding staircase was an unusual feature of this great house. From the house there was a steep descent to the springhouse, in which a continuous stream of crystal-clear water flowed. The large dairy barn stood on a knoll in the background.

The one thing I remember best about this place of many beauties, however, was the pasture in the southwest corner of the farm. This contained some forty-odd acres of natural woodland, consisting mostly of magnificent oak and maple trees. From a level plain there gradually rose a hill of considerable size. A stream cut through the pasture at the foot of the hill, and from the summit one could see across the entire countryside for miles to the north. This was the most picturesque setting for a herd of black and white cows that one could imagine. Day after day, I climbed to the top of this hill and sank down heavily into the deep grass, to rest after the hard jaunt up the ridge — and to plan the future.

And so April drifted into May.

At Rose Harbor I learned the proper method of milking cows by machine. At Arnewood I had always hand-milked my cows. Paul Behn was using the Surge Milker in his herd with very good results. The Surge operates on a principle unlike any other mechanical milker. The machine hangs suspended by means of a leather belt or surcingle fastened around the cow's belly; this belt can be placed forward on the animal's back after the teat cups are applied, giving just enough "pull" to make the pail act as a pendulum, surging back and forth, the action increasing as more milk in the pail gives added pull for those last drops of milk in the udder. When this machine is properly hung, after the correct stimulus is applied to the udder by a gentle massaging with a very warm cloth to give a complete letdown of milk, cows will usually milk out dry in about two minutes without further stripping.

The manner and judgment of the operator of a milker is of greater importance than the type of machine used. I was indeed fortunate to learn this method of milking from Paul, whom I still consider the best machine-milker I have encountered.

One morning in late May, I made my usual trip to the top of the hill in the pasture. The day was particularly resplendent. My whole being was vibrant with excitement and radiant health. How different I was from the puny little fellow my father used to take with him out into the country while he was building roads. There is a source of vitality one draws from the land and from working with the animals that feed upon it, as well as the pleasure one derives in doing something one loves.

The spring air was filled with the scent of crabapple blossoms that grew in profusion on the hill, and with the sweet musical notes of the robin and meadow lark. The grass stretched out in an almost endless sea to the fields of corn and oats that lay in contours and terraces as far away as the eyes could see. The corn was just high enough so that it could be rowed easily even from a distance.

I sprawled on the grass and viewed this scene. The black and white cows ate luxuriously of the luscious forage. Spread out before me, I saw and realized the greatest crop on earth, grass, and the Holstein cow, the most efficient convertor of this plant into man's best food.

Yes, I was satisfied now that I had chosen the black and white cow. I had made no mistake. The facts were indisputable. The Holstein cow is the most popular breed, as evidenced by the fact that in the most prosperous dairy sections of this country their number surpasses the total of all other breeds combined. In both milk and butterfat the black and white cow holds all of the world's records in all classes over all breeds. In 1947, 70 per cent of all the milk sold in the big cities came from the Holstein cow. Ninety per cent of all the institutions in this country bred Holstein cows and used Holstein milk. Holstein milk itself is most like human milk not only in the size of the fat globules and the softness of curd which makes it the most easily digestible of all milk, but also in that the butterfat content of Holstein and human milk is the same — 3.5 per cent. Since the dawn of the world, man has been reared on 3.5 per cent milk, positive proof that it is still the best balance for him. The government paid high tribute to the black and white cow when it established 3.5 per cent milk for our fighting men. The pure white color of Holstein milk, sometimes fallaciously assailed, is one of its crowning virtues. Science has shown that yellow-colored milk does not measure increased fat content, but indicates the inability of cows producing such milk to convert carotin into Vitamin A. Since many persons are unable to convert carotin into

Vitamin A, they must depend upon the cow to do this job for them. Research has shown that Holstein milk may contain as much as 60 per cent more pure Vitamin A than does yellow milk.

I was thoroughly convinced of the superiority of the black and white cow. Which of us can measure the debt that civilization owes this noble animal or, realizing it, give her the credit and care she so rightly deserves?

The hours passed more quickly than I had realized. The cows had filled themselves with the earth's great bounty, and were resting on the hillside. Slowly I rose to my feet. I had reached a decision. Melvin Campbell had extended me a standing invitation to come to Maytag Dairy Farms even before the dispersal of my own herd, and now I was ready to accept. The Maytag herd had been established for twenty-five years, following a program of close breeding to the very heart of the Ormsbys. Here I would have the opportunity to observe and to learn the things I wanted to know. And my innate love for Iowa had turned the scale in favor of the Maytag herd.

☆ XIII ☆

The Maytag Dairy Farms

THE HEAVY SPRING rains during the months of April and May of 1944 caused great floods in southern Iowa. The Des Moines and Skunk rivers had turned loose their fury over thousands of fertile acres of land, and had completely isolated several towns and cities. Several bridges and huge sections of railroad tracks were washed away by the inundation. Electric power, telephone service, and the mails were disrupted for several weeks. Then, too, there was the ever-present threat of disease that follows in the wake of every major flood.

118

By June, when I arrived at the Maytag Dairy Farms at Newton, the rains had become less frequent, and the swollen streams had receded somewhat; nevertheless, there were still a great many fields under water, and others so wet that they could not be planted to corn. This was a new experience for me, since I had never known the terror of floods in northern Iowa.

The Maytag Dairy Farms had not been affected to any extent by the floods in that section. The buildings themselves were nestled on a hillside against a background of pine, walnut, oak, and elm trees. The valley was well drained, and the pastures lay south of the main line of barns on gently rising terrain.

As I drove over the brow of the hill overlooking the farm, I received an impressive view of the dairy. I remembered every detail from my visit four years previously. To the left and across the road from the main set of buildings was a lone white barn in which every calf was started on a nurse cow. South and west of this nurse cow barn was an thirty-acre pasture, wooded in the southwest corner, in which the dry cows and pregnant heifers were allowed to graze and to condition themselves for freshening. To the right a paved road led off the main graveled highway through the beautifully landscaped yards in front of the modern buildings. Directly off the highway, and prominently set off from it on a higher elevation, was the manager's home, surrounded by well-trimmed box hedges. Next to it was the office and the modern dairy where the milk was cooled, pasteurized, and bottled. In this dairy also was made the famous blue-veined Maytag Cheese, and back of it were the caves dug into the hillside where the cheese was aged three months before it was sold. The main milking barn was just off from the creamery, and, like the rest of the barns, faced west. This one large dairy barn, however, had a wing to the south in which the test cows were kept. Adjoining the calf barn, which was next in line, was the bull barn with its individual, stoutly reinforced exercise pens. To the extreme right lay the open shed-type barn which housed the dry stock in winter, and served as a fitting barn for the show herd during the summer.

Melvin Campbell, the efficient manager, was expecting me when I entered the office on that early June morning. He welcomed me with a warm handshake, and offered me a chair. Mr. Campbell had that rare combination of affable manners and informal speech which instantly made one feel as if he had known the man for a long time. The telephone on his desk rang sharply, and while he was answering it, I took the opportunity to look around the room.

This office was unique in the fact that on its walls hung perhaps more blue ribbons, premier awards, and trophies than were owned by any other herd of Holstein cattle in the world. From 1931 until 1947, the name Maytag blazed a trail of glamour on the tanbark, the like of which had never been known before in the dairy world. During that time the Maytag herd had won more All-American winnings in the show rings of North America than any other herd. Back in the late twenties, young Bob Stewart, unknown then to the public, came to the farm. Under the Maytag banner he learned all the tricks of the show ring and became the outstanding showman of the country. His grace and finesse in handling the animals of the Maytag herd in the shows of this country and Canada, and his graciousness to both spectators and judges alike, won high acclaim for him over a period of years. Under his masterful training Maytag animals achieved unprecedented favor in the public eye. He is now an official with the American Guernsey Club, with offices at Peterborough, New Hampshire.

I shall have to confess to some misgivings on my part as Mel Campbell took me out to the barn to introduce me to Jock McCormack, the man who had been in charge of the Maytag herd for more than fifteen years. On my former visit to Maytags I had missed meeting the well-known herdsman, but I had heard a great deal about him. I had imagined him to be a stern man with a fiery temperament, and I had dreaded all along the ordeal of meeting him.

We found Mr. McCormack milking one of the test cows by hand. I discovered later that she was Jock's favorite, a cow named Inka Rue Ollie Posch, and the only member of the herd that was hand-milked. The rest of the herd was milked with the Surge Milker, and I was glad that it was the machine I had already become acquainted with. For the past twenty-five years, the test cows had been milked four times a day. During the war years, when labor was so hard to get, the Maytag herd was one of the last herds to stay by 4x milking.

After Jock McCormack had finished milking his cow, he offered me his hand and said smilingly, mixing his rich Scotch brogue with his good English, "Hi, ya! So you're the new mon Mel has been telling me about?"

"That's right," I said, clasping his firm hand. "I'm real pleased to meet you."

Jock had an uncanny ability for detecting superficiality and hypocrisy in men on first acquaintance. I soon discovered this trait in him, a thing that most of his friends had known for a long time. If one passed this first meeting successfully, he was Jock's friend for life.

Jock McCormack's features were pleasant, if not whimsical. His hair was white now, with a long strand continually falling down over his forehead. Summer and winter, I learned, his head remained uncovered. The eyes were soft and sparkling, but as they looked at you, they seemed to penetrate deep into your mind. The mouth was fine, but with lines around it, and the clean-cut chin beneath hinted of firmness. He was of medium stature and weight; his gait was shuffling, owing to the fact that his feet had become crippled while in military service. During front-line action there had been periods as long as twenty-three days and nights at a time when he had never been able to remove his shoes.

I met this great cowman on that tenth day of June, 1944, little dreaming then of the progress we would make together, or of the bond of friendship that was to tie us over the years. We were as different from each other as two human beings could possibly be; yet, from the moment of our first acquaintance, there was a complete and mutual understanding between us.

For over a quarter of a century Jock McCormack had been one of the most colorful figures in Holstein circles, and in that time had contributed much to Iowa and Holstein history. It was back in 1913 that a sandy-haired boy of twenty left his home in Kirkcudbright, Scotland, to meet a relative in Waterloo, Iowa, who had promised him a job. When Jock arrived in Waterloo, his relative had moved away, leaving the boy on his own. His first job was with a poultry concern. Although the youth had never had any experience in this line, he pretended to know everything there was to know about the business. After receiving the job, Jock studied poultry books at night to learn the management of poultry flocks. The chickens had been dying by the hundreds. Jock knew without any experience that the chicken houses needed a thorough job of cleaning and disinfecting. After a period of six weeks, Jock had a healthy flock on full production.

"If you're not willing to take responsibility, you'll never get anywhere," he once told me.

His experience with poultry was at the Galloway Farm. That same fall they placed Jock in full charge of their show herd at Waterloo, where, among other winnings, he took grand championship at the Dairy Cattle Congress with Fay Jewel Beauty. When the Galloway Farm herd was dispersed shortly after, Jock worked for a time with Charles Nelson of Waverly, Iowa; then he showed cattle for Hugh Van Pelt. In 1915 he went to Colonel French's Iowana Farms at Davenport, then one of the nation's great Holstein herds. At Iowana, Jock handled the fourteen-year-old Waterloo grand champion, Lady Johanna Aaggie Fayne. Iowana, under Colonel French, was one of the early advocates of 3x milking. One of the famous families developed at that time was the Fryslan Waldorf family. Jock completed an 800-pound record on Fryslan Waldorf, and records of over 800 pounds fat on three of her daughters.

In 1916, before the United States entered the first World War, Jock asked his good friend, Colonel French, for a leave of absence. He joined the 50th Battalion of the Canadian Army, and was soon on the front lines in France with a machine gun squadron. This squadron was shifted from one sector of the front to another and was sent over into No-Man's-Land in advance of the front-line troops to cover them as they went over the top. For this reason it was called the Flying Squadron. Theirs was one of the most dangerous of front-line types of action. Almost every time the squadron was changed to a different sector, it received new replacements as Jock's buddies were killed. In one engagement, only Jock and two of his pals survived. After two years of this, the war was over, and Jock, after visiting his mother in Scotland, returned to Iowana Farms.

After twelve years at Iowana, Jock came to Maytag Dairy Farms with Orin Hatch, who had been manager at Iowana Farms, and who had become manager at Maytags. That was in 1926, the first year that E. H. Maytag started a small circuit of fairs. Jock showed the first prize four-year-old, M. B. Ormsby Wayne, at Waterloo. During the three succeeding years, he worked with the test cows as well as taking out the show herd, and made several 800-pound records at Maytags. When Mr. Hatch resigned as manager in 1929, Jock left Maytags and showed cattle for the Iowa Board of Control.

Many interesting stories are told about Jock during this part of his life, when the thrill of the tanbark surged through his veins. Unpretentious himself, Jock would be the last to admit any of them.

On several occasions, while showing cattle at different fairs throughout the country, Jock would watch the judges reviewing an especially large class of animals. It is customary for a judge to sort out ten or more individuals in his first line-up to go back to the barn. Sometimes in this group there may be an outstanding animal, but because the showman is not on his toes and does not show his animal properly at just the moment when the judge rests his attention on that animal, it is picked out at the first weeding and sent out of the ring. Jock McCormack knew a good animal when he saw one, and he knew the value of good showmanship. If an animal was especially deserving in his opinion, he might lead it back into the ring himself. He might pretend to be bringing in a late entry, and get away with the gag as only Jock could. With Jock at the halter, showing it properly, the judge on many such occasions has given the animal the purple ribbon, not knowing that he had previously disqualified it.

It was while Jock was showing for Maytags in 1927 at the Iowa State Fair in Des Moines that he approached the manager of the Hargrove and Arnold herd, who was also showing at the same fair. Jock had missed a certain heifer in their string that he had seen just once before, and had admired. That was the previous year when she had been beaten in Illinois.

"Where's the little speckled heifer you had at Springfield last year?" he asked Ray Arnold.

"She got beat there, didn't she?" was the laconic reply. "There wasn't any use bringing her here this year."

"I don't care for the opinion of one judge. She's the best dom heifer I've ever seen!" Jock exclaimed. "Put her in your show herd, and fit her up a bit. Take my word for it, there's nothing can beat her."

After some time Jock persuaded Hargrove and Arnold to go home after their senior yearling heifer. Their herd was at Norwalk, not far from Des Moines. The heifer was taken right out of the pasture without any fitting. She placed third at the Iowa State Fair. Her owners were thoroughly disgusted, not only with the animal but with Jock as well.

"No use sending her along on the big-time circuit," they told him, "if she can't do better than that at her own state fair. We're going to send her back to the farm — and for good!"

"Don't do it!" Jock said emphatically. "What of it? She got a raw deal, boys. She's a little thin after just calving and showed rather badly today, but she'll snap out of it; and by the time you make the next fair, she'll be looking like a million dollars. Give her jist one more chance, boys, jist," he pleaded, using a favorite expression of his whenever he wished to emphasize his point, "and I'll bet you she'll not take another beating."

That heifer was Triune Papoose Piebe, and she did not go home after this defeat. The Holstein world saw her go through that season undefeated anywhere after the Iowa State Fair. After the show season was over, she became All-American Senior Yearling for 1927. Jock received a box of expensive cigars with many thanks and apologies from Hargrove and Arnold. The following year Triune Papoose Piebe was again made All-American, and for six years, from the time when she was a heifer calf until she became an aged cow, she received the All-American designation, an honor never accorded before or since to a Holstein female. Eventually she brought $11,100 in public sale, and went to Mount Victoria Farms, Hudson Heights, Quebec, where she founded with Johanna Rag Apple Pabst one of the greatest herds of Holsteins the world has ever seen.

Mel Campbell, a young man from Redwood Falls, Minnesota, had come to Maytag Dairy Farms as a cow tester in 1929. E. H. Maytag had founded the Maytag herd as a hobby, with the purpose of intensifying the Ormsby bloodlines, which he believed to be the best family in the Holstein breed. He was a quiet man, retiring by nature. His tastes were simple, and he dearly loved the soil and the Holstein cow. He had the rare faculty of surrounding himself with able assistants, and of arousing them to do their best work. His friends were very carefully chosen, and Mr. Maytag placed his every confidence in the young cow tester. When Orin Hatch resigned as manager of Maytag Dairy Farms, Mr. Maytag offered the position to Campbell.

"But I've had no experience managing such a farm," Mel Campbell hesitated, "and if you place an inexperienced person like me in charge of your herd the general public may look unfavorably upon it; and the reputation the herd has already made for itself will be ruined."

"If you'll take the job," Mr. Maytag replied, "I'll not worry about that."

"If I take the job, I should like to engage Jock McCormack to come back and be herdsman."

"I don't believe he'll come back," Mr. Maytag said. "But if you want him and if he'll come back, it'll be all right with me. If you say you'll take the job, it will make me very happy."

"I'll take it, Mr. Maytag," Mel said, "and I'll do my best."

"I know you will," E. H. Maytag said. "There is one thing, Mel, I believe we should insist on in hiring Mr. McCormack. The herd is growing now to the point where I believe the herdsman in charge should put all his time and effort in the herd, and leave the showing of the cattle to someone else. It's harmful to the herd in general for the herdsman in charge to be away from the herd for two months or such a matter during the show season."

"I believe you're right, Mr. Maytag," Mel Campbell agreed, "but I don't know how Jock will feel about giving that part of it up. You see, when a man gets the show ring in his blood, it never leaves him. When the show season comes round each year, the old feeling comes back, and it will be difficult to ask Jock to give it up."

"Yes, I know."

Jock McCormack returned to Maytag Dairy Farms early in 1932, and remained at home each year when the show herd was taken out. He became so devoted to his loving wife and two daughters that he was content to give up the excitement of the shows; but on the occasions when Jock recalled the many stories of his experiences on the show circuit, I could note the old flame burning inside him, and the glamour of the tanbark that was gone now forever.

But at the farm he was busy. He had direct charge of the test cows and calves, as well as general supervision of the entire herd. At Maytag Farms, he has completed forty-two records exceeding 800 pounds fat, and seven records over 1,000 pounds fat. The whole breed is deeply indebted to this man for his accomplishments and for his rich personality that has dominated the sale rings and show rings of the breed for so many years. In giving credit to achievements in this great breed of ours, the industry is prone to overlook the man who is responsible for so much of its success, the man who works with the cows themselves, who almost lives with them, feeding and caring for them when everything goes along smoothly, ministering to them when they are sick, waiting up long hours during the night to assist them in calving.

Jock loved to recall his associations with E. H. Maytag. A strong bond of friendship had grown up between these two. It became almost a routine with "E.H.," as he was affectionately called, to drive out to the farm for the midnight milking, and to chat with Jock while he fed the test cows.

"Nothing pleased him more," Jock once reminisced, "than when a bull he had sold to some other breeder would take the blue ribbon away from an animal shown by Maytags."

Although the first animals in the Maytag herd were purchased in 1919, it was not until 1930 that the herd began to be known. From its very inception, the aim was to keep as close to Sir Pietertje Ormsby Mercedes and his son "37th" as possible, by intensifying their blood through their sons and daughters. These two Ormsby sires are generally conceded to be the greatest sires in the Holstein breed. The Maytag herd carried more of the close-up blood of these two sires than any other herd in the country.

Sir Pietertje Ormsby Mercedes 37th's greatest son was a bull called Man-O-War, the name taken from the illustrious horse. Maytags had already become interested in the Man-O-War line not only because of his remarkable line-bred pedigree, but also because the daughters of Man-O-War were beginning to make history. Arrangements were made during the summer of 1930 for the purchase of the bull himself from the Wm. Schmidt's Sons herd, St. Peter, Minnesota, breeders of all the Man-O-War daughters. The bull was a massive individual, weighing over three thousand pounds. When he arrived in Newton he had been injured during shipment, and had to be hauled out to the farm on a stoneboat. He was placed under the trees on the hill where he lay for several days. When it was finally learned his condition was hopeless, old Man-O-War was mercifully put out of his misery.

The following March, Maytags went back to Minnesota and purchased seven daughters of the old bull, and each year through 1935 they continued gathering together all the daughters of this bull that they could obtain, twenty-three in all. Man-O-War stock soared to dizzy heights of popularity when Maytags brought out the winning Get of Sire in 1931, 1932, 1933, and again in 1934, to give Man-O-War the distinction, which he still holds, of being the only sire to win the coveted All-American Get four different years. In 1938 the Get of Man-O-War was to be named All-Time All-American Get of Sire.

Among the daughters of old Man-O-War were Esther, Pearl, Betty, Irene, Little Lassie, and Lassie Maid, cows that have seldom if ever been equaled for combined type with production. The favorite of all of these was Esther, who made 1,093 pounds fat on 4x milking, and was three times in the All-American Get of Sire groups.

The well-deserved popularity of the Man-O-War line received its deathblow by the fraudulent practices of their unscrupulous breeders. The integrity of the Maytag herd itself was at stake. The breeders of the Man-O-War line, hoping to clean up a fortune through the fame of their cattle, devised the clever ruse of buying calves of nondescript origin from their neighbors' herds, and registering them as twins to their own calves as Man-O-War offspring. For a time this worked, and there were several spurious Man-O-Wars sold to the gullible public. When the practice was discovered, the Minnesota herd was exposed, and an attempt was made to straighten out the affair and to determine the rightful offspring of Man-O-War. The herd was forced to disperse, and under the rules of the association forever barred from registering cattle in that association. Because there was still the question whether an animal was rightfully a Man-O-War, the whole affair was given a black eye, and the prestige of the Maytag herd suffered a terrific blow, despite the fact that no Maytag animals were involved. The years that have elapsed have proved to the Holstein public that the Maytag herd had been an innocent victim of the fraud and thereby suffered the most because of the affair; the years have testified to the integrity and unselfish devotion to the breed of E. H. Maytag, and no mere tribute will suffice for this man who was so valiant in this fight. Only time has given Man-O-War and his wonderful daughters the acclaim they deserved; and who can say what brilliant accomplishments they might have brought to their breed had not their brightness been extinguished so prematurely?

To succeed Man-O-War, Maytags purchased from Detroit Creamery Farms the sire, DeCreamCo Calamity Posch, for $15,000. Again this bull carried an intensification of the blood of 37th.

At the Royal Brentwood Sale in 1931 another sire was purchased. He was a son of Wisconsin Fobes 7th, one of the very greatest daughters of old 37th. His name was Posch Ormsby Fobes. An amusing sidelight occurred at this sale. When Posch Ormsby Fobes was brought into the ring to be sold, Mel Campbell shouted out a $1,000 bid for the bull calf. Maytags had been determined to get this young sire. All eyes were instantly focused on this young greenhorn in whose hands the destiny of the Maytag herd rested. There was silence. No one challenged the opening bid. The young manager from Maytags flushed; perhaps there were chuckles in the crowd. Posch Ormsby Fobes might have been bought for considerably less money.

The Holstein organization was soon to learn, however, that E. H. Maytag had made a wise choice in his new manager. In the years that followed they saw in the young manager one of the shrewdest buyers in the game, and one of the very best salesmen of all time, even if he had had to learn salesmanship by writing to all the big herds in America asking about certain bulls they had offered for sale, just to see how they wrote their bull letters!

In the famous Walters dispersal in 1938 Maytags acquired the heart of that great herd, twenty-one head in all. These animals were mostly sons and daughters of Sir Bess Ormsby Fobes 73rd, a grandson of old 37th, thus continuing their very definite line-breeding program. One of the cows purchased at this time was Ermvale Dinah Korndyke Ormsby, who was thirteen years old. Maytags hoped to get the calf she was carrying by the service of 73rd, which would make it a full brother or sister to the young sire they purchased in the same sale, Sir Bess Ormsby Dean. Old Dinah not only dropped the calf they were hoping for, but lived to be past twenty years of age and dropped five calves in the Maytag herd. Her son, Dean, was to become one of the great proved sires in Iowa. After many years' service in the Maytag herd, Dean was sold to Dairy Genetics, Des Moines, Iowa, one of the country's big artificial insemination rings. Here he spent his last days.

Another sire was making quite a name for himself in the State Institution herd at Cherokee, Sir Ormsby Fobes Dictator, and he was bred much the same way as the other sires already in service at Maytags. With the purchase of Dictator, the future of the Maytag herd was assured. Once again its fame spread far and wide.

ERMVALE DINAH KORNDYKE ORMSBY — (OLD DINAH)
Most Efficient 19-year-old Cow with 16th Calf — Maytag Sixteenth Dinah

SIR BESS ORMSBY DEAN — SON OF OLD DINAH
Won *Wallaces' Farmer* Dairy Sire Contest
Sold to Dairy Genetics in Des Moines

TWO FAMOUS SIRES AND THEIR GRANDSONS

MAN-O-WAR   SIR ORMSBY FOBES DICTATOR

MAN-O-WAR PROGRESSOR   MAYTAG ORMSBY FOBES DICTATOR

✩ XIV ✩

Jock McCormack

JOCK MCCORMACK taught me many things about dairy cows that I needed to know; his lifetime of experience with them had given him a knowledge of cows and cowmen second to none in this country. I was fortunate in being able to work with this man at a time when I was increasing my own powers of observation and insight into this fine art; all of which was to stand me in good stead when the time would come for me to apply this education — a time that was then very near at hand.

The first two or three months at Maytags were a dizzy whirl of activity in which I was being converted to a new aspect of dairying very different from what I had been used to at Arnewood. There was an ever-present stir of excitement and an inescapable atmosphere of glamour inseparable from life at Maytag Dairy Farms. I caught this feeling from the start and soon became a part of it.

There were almost daily visitors from all parts of the country, some of them coming for the purpose of selecting a new herd sire for their herds, still others merely to see the famous breeding establishment. Jock told me that before the war brought restrictions on gas and travel, there had been a greater number of visitors to the farm, not only from this country and Canada but from lands as far distant as Africa and Japan.

At Arnewood I had always sketched the markings of every new-born calf on the back of the applications for registration. At Maytags, where there were so many calves being born almost daily, pictures were taken of every calf as soon as it was born; in fact, two pictures were taken, one of each side of the calf, to be used for identification and registration. This was a comparatively simple matter, however, since these pictures were never used for publicity purposes. But when the calf grew older, especially the bull calves, which would be sold more often by mail than by actual personal selection, another picture would be taken. This time the calf would have to be specially scrubbed and groomed for the occasion, and then carefully posed. This required time, diligence, skill, and patience. But when animals are to be sold at great distances, the buyer must rely almost entirely on a picture, and this "eye appeal" cannot be underestimated. Alertness is the keynote in every animal picture. True, a bull with his head down is just as good a one as a bull with his head up, but not when you are trying to sell that bull. With a cow the problem is even more difficult. She must have her picture taken at just the right time when she is looking her best, and that particular time is when she is in bloom, just prior to freshening. Sometimes you have only a few hours' warning, and not infrequently the old "blister" will calve before you get the chance to snap her. The weather creates an additional problem in getting good pictures. But the all-important thing is to get her picture, and to get a good one that will best show off her rump, her udder, and her topline. She must be posed by someone who is skilled in just this knack of handling a cow. It takes a second person to snap the picture, and that person must know how to take a good picture and when to take it. The subject should not be taken against the manure spreader or a broken-down fence or barn. Her head must be up and her ears forward. Her legs must stand squarely under her, and, if she could talk, you know she would ask, "What's that?" At just the instant when the cow would make this statement, the photographer must snap the picture. There are devices especially designed for this purpose. They are performed by a third person who keeps himself hidden at just the right position. When the cameraman is ready to take the picture, the man in hiding steps out with an umbrella — it should be a red one. (Cows are not color blind as they are thought to be. I have seen them rush to a spot where a yellow goldenrod was blooming in the grass, deceived into believing it was an ear of corn.) But as soon as the cow guesses what the umbrella is, the opportunity is over, and the one chance you may have been waiting hours for is gone. Mel Campbell, the manager, has always taken the pictures of the Maytag animals for most advertising purposes, and readers of the *World* will agree that the pictures coming from this establishment are as good as the best professional animal pictures. I remarked to Jock one day about this.

"Mel certainly takes fine pictures for an amateur," I said.

"Amateur, hell!" he returned. "He's been taking pictures for fifteen years!"

When I first came to the farm, I was amazed at the amount of time spent in washing walls and ceilings in the barns. The work seemed endless and tiresome, but I gradually became accustomed to it. Not that cleanliness was unheard of at Arnewood, but in the old barn that I had been used to I never thought of washing the walls. At Maytags the first thing a novice notices is the quick turnover of brooms used in the barns. There is almost as much time spent in sweeping floors and alley-ways as is spent in actual milking and feeding.

I am thankful to Jock for calling my attention to these tiny particulars. They are often overlooked by the average dairyman, and yet they mean a great deal. Every day the water cups in all barns were checked to see that the animals had not contaminated them with manure, a fact which would keep them from drinking water. In a herd of two hundred head of cattle the job of trimming feet becomes one of the biggest chores, and certainly one of the most dangerous.

A watchful eye in this direction will often save an animal from going lame. One of the more exciting tasks was connected with this particular job — that of throwing the main herd bulls in order to trim their feet. It requires the assistance of six husky men on the rope to drop one of these massive animals. There is a certain amount of skill required to trim feet quickly and correctly, and at the same time to keep out of the way of the enraged animal's kicking.

One day when we were throwing the nearly three thousand pound Dean bull, he got loose from the men. The man at the halter fell under the great bull, but escaped being trampled on. The Dean bull was usually a very gentle animal and was trusted. It was only the bull's quiet nature and his desire to get away from the men that perhaps saved this event from being a disastrous one.

Perhaps the most striking thing done on this farm when I came to it was the milking job itself. For almost twenty-five years the test cows had been milked four times a day, or regularly every six hours. For these twenty test cows that were milked on a 4x schedule, the hours of milking were 5 a.m., 11 a.m., 5 p.m., and 11 p.m. Jock handled these cows personally, and until the last few years it had been customary for the barn men to get one day off in seven weeks. Little wonder then that Jock was a sound sleeper and had to be awakened sometimes; little wonder he had but a few hours at home with his family in the evening; little wonder it was an actual fact that Jock and his wife in the period of their marriage had never had a quarrel! The balance of the milking herd was run on a twice-a-day milking schedule, and was not tested. To tie in with the 4x milking, the regular herd was milked at about 4 a.m. and 3:30 p.m. Being a light sleeper myself, I was completely befuddled at first by the sound of alarm clocks going off at all hours of the day and night in the dormitory, and of men getting up and going to bed at all hours.

As the weeks and months passed, I learned to know Jock better and to like the man. Jock McCormack is the sort of person whom one meets and never forgets. Almost every Holstein man in the country knows and loves Jock, but they see him only as a man who understands his cows and loves them, a man with an infectious, enviable profanity, a man who is the life of every sale and show he attends. But few know the gentle heart and tender emotions that pulse beneath this reckless, jovial outward personality.

His Scotch phrases in his own inimitable brogue rolled from his tongue so fast that it was impossible to catch very many of them, and at first it was a problem for me to understand him at all. I recall with a chuckle the time when Jock gave these instructions to one of the men: "This afternoon I want you to wash the coo tills."

Almost everyone knew that to Jock a cow was a coo, but a till was another matter. When Jock got up to milk in the afternoon, he questioned the man about the task he had left him to do.

"I thought I told you to wash the coo tills. Why didn't you do it?"

"But I did, Jock," was the reply, pointing to the feed mangers. "I washed every one of them."

Jock laughed. He had meant for the man to wash the cows' tails, and the man, not knowing just what tills were, thought they must be the mangers.

Jock clung to the tradition of his beloved Scotland. He never learned to operate an automobile, but summer and winter he might be seen riding back and forth from the farm to his home on a bicycle. He carried his vehicle over the snowdrifts, and laughed at those who were stuck in the drifts with their cars.

Evenings when he came out for the midnight milking, he would come to my room and talk with me. One evening he came to my room and, sitting down on the edge of my bed, began a discussion of the relative merits of great sires and great dams.

"Some bulls are sires of great daughters," Jock said, "while others sire great sons. Man-O-War's daughters were all great cows, but he never had a single noteworthy son. Dictator was known for his marvelous daughters."

"I see what you mean," I answered. "I had never thought of that angle of it. I suppose you would put Woodmaster in the same category?"

"Yes. On the other hand," Jock continued, "there was Posch Ormsby Fobes, whose sons were sensational. There was Posch Ormsby Fobes 11th, the highest index sire in the United States, and Posch Ormsby Fobes 6th, the great proved sire at the University of Arizona. Greatest of them all was Winterthur's Posch Ormsby Fobes 14th, leading honor list sire of them all for several years."

"The question in my mind is where did these great sires derive their greatness then — from their own sires or from their dams?" I asked. "In other words, which do you think is more important, great sires or great brood cows?"

"That's a matter that many great masters of breeding differ on. Some put most importance on the sire, while others place stress on great cows."

"I have given the subject a great deal of thought," I ventured, "and have decided that even though great sires are scarce, there are more of them known to the breed than there are great brood cows, and the influence of a bull can be more widely diffused than that of a cow, because he can have several hundred offspring. Nevertheless, I am inclined to place greater emphasis on great brood cows. In this respect, I am in accord with the viewpoint of both the Carnation people and Paul Misner, whose opinions I regard highly."

"I have known several cow families," I continued, "that were weak from the production standpoint, and even though they were mated with great proved sires for several generations, the cows still did not produce satisfactorily. On the other hand, you may take a cow that comes from a long line of great producers, mate her with a mediocre bull, and still get a great producer. I believe if a herd is made up of cow families that have for generations proved themselves to be great producers, a poor bull can be brought into that herd without ruining, in one generation, the production that has been carefully bred into the herd for generations. In herds that are continually striving for a succession of proved bulls without particular stress on cow families, the use of just one poor sire will tear down all the production that has been bred into the herd over a period of many years."

"I believe you're right about that point," Jock agreed. "There's Dunloggin Woodmaster, for instance. Every breeder knows he was out of Mother Pearl herself, but how many people know the name of his sire? All the great bulls had great dams, Governor of Carnation, Sensation, Sir Bess Ormsby Dean, Sir Pietertje Ormsby Mercedes, and Dunloggin Design are but a few. If we put greater stress on great brood cow families, I believe, like you, that great sires will take care of themselves."

"Then there are those who'll tell you that if you're purchasing heifers you should prefer to have them sired by a great bull, and place less importance on the cows they are out of; but when you are buying bulls you should be more particular about their dams than their sires," I said, leading away from the subject we had been discussing. "Also it has been said that the first calves from a great brood cow are nearly always to be preferred to those dropped after the cow becomes old. I would rather want to believe, though, that the last calf from a good cow is equally as good as her first."

"There are a great many questions about dairying still unanswered," Jock replied. "There is much yet to learn. There'll be many discoveries in the next few years. Men are becoming more concerned about improving our breed, and in extending the influence of the great animals within our breed whenever they are found by every means they can. Just as artificial insemination, a tool only practiced on a wide scale within the last few years, has been a most remarkable means of spreading the influence of our proved sires, so will a way be found wherein the superior blood of our great brood cows will be disseminated in order that a larger number of progeny may be acquired from one cow than is now possible."

"There is such a possibility now being considered by the transplanting of an egg from a superior cow into the uterus of a mediocre cow, called an incubator cow," I replied.

"I have heard of it once or twice," Jock said, "but how would it work?"

"A cow ovulates once every three weeks or such a matter," I explained. "Now if some method can be found whereby the egg expelled from the ovary of one cow could be isolated somewhere along its path from the fallopian tubes into the uterus, and then transplanted into the uterus of another cow, by simple arithmetic it would be possible for one cow to have as many as seventeen calves in one year instead of only one."

"But how would one know whether the incubator cow was growing a calf from her egg or a calf from the egg of a good cow?" Jock wondered.

"The egg from the incubator cow would have to be found also during the period of ovulation and destroyed before the superior egg could be transplanted. Of course there would be the possibility of two eggs being laid during one heat period, one from each ovary. But any veterinarian can tell by rectal examination if one or both ovaries are passing an egg, by simply feeling for the follicle on the ovary."

"But is such a plan really possible?" Jock asked dubiously.

"When I first heard of it I, too, thought it sounded too fantastic ever to be accomplished," I replied, "but I spoke to a specialist in the field of sterility, and he said that such an idea was entirely possible but not feasible at present. It could not be done by a layman as is artificial insemination; it would require the skill of a technician. It would, therefore, be used only in extreme cases so that a sensational cow might have a greater number of calves. For the present, then, it must remain a challenge to our ingenuity."

(A few years after this conversation, in March, 1951, an issue of the *Farm Journal* carried a report of an actual case where a fertilized egg had been taken from a cow and transferred to a foster mother. The following issue of the paper published a picture of the live calf nursing its "incubator" mother; his own mother had died nine months before his birth.)

Sometimes we both became so absorbed in our conversation that we did not realize that the hours had passed so quickly — that it was time to milk again. Jock would change his clothes, slipping out of his good ones into his work pants and shoes. In the barn he wore the same pair of shoes all the time I knew him. There was a sort of perennial quality about them, except the shoe laces, which were often replaced with beet pulp strings. Jock had a peculiarity from which he never deviated. He always put on his left sock and shoe first. If he ever picked up his right shoe first, he always set it down again and reached for his left one.

Jock was married back in the summer of 1930, just before the fall show season began. His pretty young wife, Eva, went along with Jock when he attended shows at the nearby towns in Iowa, which were at Des Moines and Waterloo. Because of the bustle and excitement that accompanies the big-time circuit, the show boys eat irregularly and more or less frequently, their hunger never seeming to be satisfied. Jock always insisted that his wife go with him for a snack. After a while this was more than she could take; she continued to go with him, but she declined eating with him. Naturally the rest of the fellows noticed this, which occasion gave rise to much ribbing of Jock for his Scotch parsimoniousness. On one occasion, Archie Sandberg, herdsman of the Green Bay Reformatory in Wisconsin, called the waiter and asked him to bring Eva a fork because Jock was too Scotch to buy more than one plate.

When their second child was born, a daughter, Jock suggested a name for her.

"I want her to be called Antonette," he told his wife.

"The name is beautiful, honey," Eva said, always using that endearing expression, "but it should be written Antoinette."

"Oh, no, not for a Scotsman!" he argued. "Why use an extra letter when it's silent anyway?"

The girl's name is spelled "Antonette."

Only those who know Jock McCormack intimately know that his Scotch stinginess is only a joke, for he is the soul of generosity. I have seen him lavish on his family everything they could wish for. When he was first married, he gave his wife a thousand-dollar cash wedding present, and in every letter he sent her while away on the show circuit there was money, from twenty to one hundred dollars. It was a tragic thing that little Antonette should suffer from asthma as a child. There were times when the frail, lovely, and musically talented child could not leave her room, which was equipped with a special air-conditioning machine. The very real devotion of Jock for this afflicted child, and hers for her daddy, was something very beautiful indeed.

One day during that first summer at Maytags, Mr. Campbell approached me while I was at work in the barn.

"Say, Mel," he began, clearing his throat.

"Yes, Mel," I answered, while we both smiled with the amusement attached to the identity of our names.

"Jock wants you to become his assistant." Again he cleared his throat. "Are you interested?"

"I'm pleased to hear it," I replied. "I consider it a great privilege."

"You're aware, I'm sure, of the duties involved. They'll include feeding the regular milking herd, besides supervising the actual milking of those cows; watching for heat periods and assisting Jock with the breeding; observing and counting the heifers and dry cows in the different pastures once a day — sometimes animals abort out in the pasture, and with this daily observation they can be detected early and isolated from the rest of the herd before there's any great danger of spreading infection in case there is any present; working with the men during the day when Jock is resting; seeing that Jock is called at milking time (he is a sound sleeper, you know!). In a word, you will become the schedule man, seeing that things are done at the proper time. Both Jock and I are confident that you'll be able to discharge these duties very well."

"I'll do my best," I promised.

This position gave me the further opportunity of getting acquainted in the shortest possible time with the details connected with the herd from the smallest calf to the bellowing herd sires.

In the fall the state Holstein sale was held at Spencer, Iowa, and I had the opportunity of accompanying Mr. Campbell to that event. Both Mel and Jock had decided they would bring to Maytags one of the animals that had been bred in my old herd, realizing it would give me an added interest at Maytags. The animal selected was none other than Arnewood Amy, the daughter of the Princess cow. Amy was at the time in a small herd near Clear Lake, Iowa, which we would pass on our way back from Spencer. It was with this idea in mind that Mel Campbell asked me to accompany him to the state sale.

Arnewood Amy was purchased by Maytag Dairy Farms, and in December she dropped a heifer calf. There was the question whether to put her on test in the 4x barn. Jock thoughtfully suggested that she be run on twice-a-day milking so that I would have the opportunity of handling her myself.

Amy was really a glutton, and Jock made the most of this fact by teasing me constantly.

"It's a good thing," he would say, "that all the cows aren't such big eaters as Amy, or Maytags would be bankrupted."

"But she has to eat to milk as she does," I defended my heifer.

"Yes, I know, but she eats enough to be giving a hundred pounds of milk."

Despite his grumbling over the tremendous amount of hay she ate, Jock always fed her additional hay at midnight along with the rest of his own test cows.

Jock had his own favorite, too. She was Inka Rue Ollie Posch, the cow he was hand-milking the day I first met him. Inka Rue had been milked four times a day for four lactations. Twice she had placed first in her class in the United States in production. When I came to Maytags she was milking in her fifth lactation, and was making her best record to date. Jock was hopeful she would make a thousand pounds of butterfat. She missed by just thirteen pounds, however. Inka Rue was milking over ninety pounds of milk a day, never quite reaching the hundred-pound mark. Whenever Jock had a day off or was away to a sale, I was privileged to milk this great cow, and I remembered there was only one other cow I had ever known that milked as heavily as Inka Rue. Here, then, was the one cow I had been searching for!

I had found her, but Jock had told me himself that Inka Rue was past her prime, that she had had her last chance of making a thousand pounds of fat, and had missed the mark by thirteen pounds. What right had I to expect either that I should ever have the opportunity to handle her myself or, if such a possibility were to happen, that I could hope to do better with her than the man who had handled so many high-record cows? Feeding and milking a cow every six hours is a terrific strain on an animal, and Inka Rue had gone through this for five successive lactations! The average life of a dairy cow is seven to eight years, and Inka Rue was way past that.

I tried to win the cow's affection by petting her, but she would shake her big head at me and turn away.

"She's no pet," Jock would say, "and you'll never make one out of her. She ain't much to look at either, but she sure can milk."

But I continued to watch her, and to admire her. Somehow, I could not explain why, she reminded me more of Cutie than any cow I had ever seen.

☆ XV ☆

A New Home

I HAD LEFT my mother with Aunt Jane when I came to Maytag Dairy Farm. Apartments in Newton were very hard to find, and houses for either sale or rent were still more scarce. I kept looking, however, and in late summer I got a lucky break. This is how it came about:

In my search for a house I had stopped at a place about half a mile south of the dairy farm to inquire if it was for sale. This had been earlier in the summer; and Mother, down for a visit, was with me. It was a small acreage just outside the city limits, the first house north of the present new multi-million-dollar Maytag factory. We found the owner thinning out the fruit in his pear trees back of the house.

"Good morning," I greeted the old man.

"How-de-do," he replied, as he stepped down from a stepladder and walked up to us. "You'll have to talk louder so I can hear you. Can't hear a thing out of my right ear, and very little out of my left."

"WHAT ARE YOU DOING?" I asked, smiling good-naturedly. "AREN'T YOU PICKING YOUR PEARS A LITTLE SMALL?"

He laughed pleasantly, and proceeded with alacrity to explain his horticultural practice. "The trees are so loaded with little pears that they can't all mature. If I pick off some of them, the rest'll get bigger. Notice how I take them off," he said, reaching a branch with his left hand, and very carefully sorting over the clusters of small pears with his right hand for just the ones to pluck; then with deft fingers, breaking them off one by one. "I leave the best-formed ones, and pick only the small, crooked, and sickly looking pears. I'm going to show you how to break them off. I take them in my two fingers and bend them close to the end of the stem. See how easy they break off. Nothing to it if you know how. You interested in fruit? It's gotta be born in ya. You gotta love your work to make a success. Ain't I right?"

As he talked he became so enthusiastic that he peered right into my face, and squinted with his left eye.

"Yes, sir, you're right there," I agreed amiably.

"What's that you say?" he queried, almost touching my face with his left ear.

"I SAID YOU'RE RIGHT. A FELLOW'S GOT TO LOVE HIS WORK TO BE A SUCCESS."

"Yes, that's so," he said, moving away and nodding his head in a manner that made me feel that he was agreeing with me rather than with his own statement.

I discovered that his name was Ernest Jackson, twice married, but now a widower; and that his senile mother, over ninety years of age, was living with him. Ernest Jackson himself was over seventy, of average height, of spare frame and spare living, only slightly stooped, and quite noticeably active for his years. He wore a battered straw hat over his white hair, a clean blue shirt and overalls that were faded and patched in a masculine sort of needlework. His shrewd blue eyes seldom looked away from the one he was talking with, and I could easily believe what he told me, that he could tell at first glance what kind of character a man had, his habits, his profession, and his degree of success in whatever he was doing. I discovered, too, that his love for flowers and plants was almost a fetish with him. He was at his best when he was showing Mother and me his array of flowers. When he stooped down on his hands and knees to pull dirt around the base of a plant where the rain had washed, he sifted the soil through his long fingers with a kind of devotion only he could understand. He took a liking to us from the start, and I am sure his and Mother's mutual love for flowers played no small part in this attachment. Even a man with less keen powers of observation than his could discover that Mother's affection for plants was genuine. I knew enough about the botanical kingdom to converse freely with the old fellow; but when it came to recognizing the many different plants by their true names, I was no match for Ernest.

"I'll bet you don't know what this is?" he said to me once as he had said again and again at every flower he showed us.

"Even i know that's rose moss," I replied.

"Portulaca," he corrected, and continued walking among the rows of beautiful annuals and perennials. "This is a bellamosum delphinium, my good lady," this to my mother, "and this is scabiosa."

"Yes, I know," Mother replied. "I see you have some baby's breath, too."

"Some what?" he asked, putting the left side of his head close to Mother's face.

"Baby's breath," she replied loudly.

"You mean gypsophila," he rectified.

"What is this, mr. jackson?" Mother asked, pointing to a border of dainty red-flowered lantanas. "I used to have some of them. They're so pretty around the edge of a bed."

The old man started to answer, then hesitated, as if he had the name on the end of his tongue, then had suddenly forgotten it. He scratched his head in puzzlement. "That's the way it is any more. Can't remember names like I used to. Old age, that's what it is. I can see myself going just like my mother. Oh, it's terrible. You don't know how it is. I know I'm going the same way."

"You know, mr. jackson," I said, in jest, "I'm the same way. I can't think of those names any more either."

He turned to me and laughed out loud. "You never did know them!"

Later we asked him about selling his place. He told us he had no intention of selling, but if anything ever turned up, he would surely keep us in mind. We asked him if he knew of any place around that we might either rent or buy. He knew of none. We left him, never expecting to see him or hear from him again.

It was, therefore, quite unexpectedly that Ernest Jackson called at the dairy farm late in August to see me. I had about given up hope of finding a place where Mother might come and live with me. At the office Ernest was told that he might find me upstairs in the dormitory. I was resting during the noon hour when he awakened me. He informed me that his mother was worse and he could not take care of her any longer; that his sister had taken her into her home; and that his own nervous condition was making him afraid to live in the house by himself. His son had persuaded him to sell his acreage and come to live with him in town.

I was more surprised when I learned how reasonably I could buy the place. I told Ernest that I would take it. I am sure no one knew the place was for sale. I don't believe it would have made any difference to Ernest if he had been offered more money. He wanted us to have it, and that was that. He was convinced that his flowers would have the best care in the world, and that was his chief concern.

Neither Mother nor I realized until after we bought the acreage and moved into the house how really nice it was. It was every bit as lovely as the cottage surrounded by old-fashioned flowers that one sees in paintings and is reproduced so many times on calendars. A white stone drive led in from the road to the garage. The bungalow itself was white, trimmed with willow green, and was partially hidden behind banks of bridal wreath, Indian currant, yucca, and staghorn fern-leaved sumac. Roses, climbers and ramblers both, of all colors turned the garden south of the house into a paradise of perfume and dazzling beauty. Smaller beds of hybrid tea roses, mostly the velvety-crimson Rome Glory variety, rioted beneath the larger shrubs. It would have been almost impossible to name a flower or shrub that he did not have growing somewhere in the garden.

Back of the house were the fruit trees, pears, apples, peaches, plums, and apricots; and still farther back on the other side of the alfalfa meadow stood the walnut trees, and against the fence were the impenetrable multiflora rose bushes that provided safe haven to all wild life. Of course there were raspberry and blackberry patches, strawberry and asparagus beds, and clumps of strawberry rhubarb and horse-radish.

North of the pear trees was the dovecot with a large flypen on the south that had morning sun and afternoon shade. I bought several pairs of White King pigeons and put them to work in the small build-ing. I had raised this most popular of all squab-producing breeds as a boy, and understood its fascination and worth. These giant white birds made a beautiful picture as they splashed and tumbled in their daily bath in the flypen.

Each pair was banded and usually mated for life. They had nest boxes made from orange crates in order that they might have two compartments to take up housekeeping: the most prolific pairs usually were sitting on two eggs in one nest while feeding young squabs in the other. The best feeders could produce squabs that weighed up to two pounds each in four weeks. Slit in half and fried in butter or roasted whole in the oven with dressing, there is nothing finer, no meat more easily digestible than squabs.

Pigeons have some most peculiar habits, easily discovered by anyone interested enough to watch them closely. They drink like no other bird. Instead of putting their beaks in the water and taking a sip, then raising their heads up in the air to swallow, they submerge their bills completely under water, and quench their thirst before taking their mouths out of the water. They take turns both in sitting on their eggs and in feeding the young birds. The male pigeon sits on the nest at night, while the female pigeon sits during the day. Until the squabs are ready to leave their nests, they are fed or rather stuffed with food from both parents, who first swallow the grains, then re-gurgitate into the mouths of their young. "That's the nature of the brutes," Ernest Jackson used to say.

EMPIRE ORMSBY MAN-O-WAR ESTHER

JOCK McCORMACK

Favorite Cow of E. H. Maytag and Jock McCormack

FIRST PRIZE GET OF SIRE (BY DICTATOR)
At Iowa State Fair, 1947 and 1948. *Left to right*: Queen Ollie Dictator
Marie, Dictator Fobes Pontiac, Dictator Fobes Pontiac Lass, and
Maytag Ormsby Pontiac Josephine

DICTATOR FOBES PONTIAC AND DICTATOR FOBES PONTIAC LASS
These Were All American Produce of Dam in 1948

* XVI *

I Become Maytag's Herdsman

ONE MORNING in April, 1945, Jock and I were working in the test barn as usual. We had finished cleaning out and bedding the box stalls, and had a little time on our hands before the eleven o'clock milking. Jock sat down on a bale of straw, and motioned for me to do the same.

"Say, Mel," he said, pulling a straw out of the bale and putting it to his mouth, "I've been thinking seriously lately of leaving Maytags. No, I haven't said anything to anyone else about it yet. You can keep it under your hat till I know for sure, but I'm just telling you that I want you to take over my job when I leave, if it's offered to you. I'll put in a good word for you, don't forget that."

I was very much surprised at this announcement, to say the least. I had felt all along that Jock was as much a part of the Maytag herd as the cattle themselves. In fact, E. H. Maytag had foreseen such a possibility, and had provided in his will that Mel Campbell and Jock McCormack should receive a share in the dairy farms, hoping by this means to keep them with the herd even after his death. I expressed my surprise in a few faltering words, and Jock explained his reasons for deciding to leave.

"As long as E. H. was alive, I'd never have thought of leaving. It jist isn't the same any more. Besides, sixteen years is too long to stay in one place. A fellow gets stale."

Jock tossed the straw he was chewing onto the floor, rose to his feet, and shuffled outside to the cement platform between the test barn and the calf barn. The bright sunlight silvered his white hair. He fumbled in his pockets for a package of Camels, took a cigarette from the pack, and lighted it.

"First Camels I've had for a long time. The dang things're so hard to get that if it wasn't for you and Eva helping me out, I'd jist about have to give up smoking."

I followed him to the door and sat down on the step, clasping my hands over my knees. "I don't believe you'll ever get stale," I said. "There isn't anyone else who can take your place, Jock. You know the Maytag animals for generations back, their weaknesses as well as their strong points. One has to know these things when breeding for the next generation."

Jock took a long draw on his cigarette before turning to me with an answer. "You know the herd, Mel, as well as the next one. Take the job, and if you run up against anything jist holler, and I'll help you out if I can."

"There'll be a lot of responsibility connected with the job," I commented hesitantly. "I don't know if I can carry the load."

"Remember, Mel, unless you're willing to take responsibility you'll never get anywhere," he advised; then, with a twinkle in his eyes, he smiled at me, "If I wasn't sure in my own mind that you could handle it, I wouldn't suggest you take the job."

"Now you're flattering me," I replied, hoping Jock would not notice the color that must surely come to my cheeks with this warm acknowledgment of his confidence in me. "But seriously I have had no experience in handling cows on official test."

"Don't be so modest, mon," Jock laughed. "I've been watching you handle Amy. You can get out of a cow as much or more than anyone I've ever known. Remember, if you have good cows to work with, and the feed, I know you'll do all right. If you don't have the feed, you nor anyone else can get it out of them."

He handed me a couple of letters; one of them from Rube Everly at Carnation Milk Farms, and the other from the Curtiss Candy Company Farms, Cary, Illinois. He told me I might read them, and I would understand why he couldn't refuse one of the offers.

After I had read them, he said, "I'm not so young as I was once, and I know Eva wants me to be with her more than I have been for the last sixteen years. Oh, no, she's never complained, but it isn't right. I've always wanted to work for Mr. Everly, who's always been a very good friend of mine, but I've got to go where the climate is best for Antonette. I'm having a couple days off next week. I intend going to Cary to look the place over, and I'll know for sure when I come back. They'll pay all my expenses out there and back whether I take the job or not."

"I can't bear to think of your leaving. I've learned a great deal through working with you, Jock."

"Well, Mel, you've learned all I can teach you. Now make use of it. I've enjoyed working with you, too, and would like to be able to work with you wherever I go, but it'll make it easier for me to leave if I know you'll carry on here. I do leave a happy part of my life behind me, and I owe much to the memory of E. H. Maytag. I want you to take good care of old Inka Rue. And be sure to feed the cats. No one else will." He tossed his cigarette butt to the ground, squashed it with his foot, and went back into the barn.

For the next week and especially during those days when Jock was gone, I was torn between conflicting emotions. What would it be like at Maytags when Jock was gone? Would I be worthy to succeed such a herdsman and to take over the responsibility of having charge of one of the greatest herds in the world?

Yet this was exactly what I had been aiming at for years. It was the one ambition I scarcely dared even hope for. Now I should gladly have let it slip by, if Jock would remain at Maytags.

After Jock had returned to work, I knew, by the expression on his face, that he had accepted the position at Curtiss Candy Farms.

"It's all settled," he said, as soon as we were alone. "If you could have seen the place, you'd never want to leave it. Two hundred box stalls in one barn! It's a knock-out!"

"When are you leaving?" I asked.

"The fifteenth of May."

"So soon? That's only about three weeks off."

"I'm going at that time, but my family will wait until school is out before we move the furniture. Mel will probably say something to you about the job before long, and I want you to accept. Don't be a fool. If there are any points you want to know before I leave, you'd better be thinking about them."

Mel Campbell approached me later that same day about the matter. He stopped me outside the office.

"I suppose Jock has told you he's leaving?" he began, after clearing his throat.

"Yes, he has. I was very much surprised."

"I'm sorry to learn he's going, but I've realized for years that sooner or later he would be leaving. I've known for a long time that some of the big breeders have been coaxing him away, but out of courtesy to this farm, they have held off pretty well during the war years. I've had someone in mind all along to take over his job, but Jock assures me you're well qualified and that I need look no further. I should be happy to know that you'll take it. It has been a policy here at Maytags to develop our own men, and I want to give you that chance. I was fortunate myself in the same way. So was Bob Stewart."

"I realize it's a big undertaking, and I am young," I answered, "but, if you're willing to take a chance with me, I can hardly refuse your offer."

Mel Campbell offered me his hand, and I shook it warmly. "Mel," he said with some emotion, "I'm happy to hear you say that. I've never had anyone working for me that I have enjoyed having around more than you. I mean it."

"I've enjoyed working for you in the past," I replied frankly, "and I'm sure our work together in the future will prove very interesting."

The old Dictator Dean bull bellowed loudly from his paddock under the barn, while a heifer lowed in answer from the pasture across the road. A sudden, frivolous gust of wind blew in across the valley, tussled with the pine and maple trees in the yard below the office, and threw handfuls of dust from the driveway into our faces. Together we turned and walked toward the barn.

Jock left the middle of May, and for a while the loss was very great. There never again would be anyone quite like him at Maytags. There was no one quite like him anywhere else. But of all the people at the farm who missed his presence, none missed him more than I.

In June I had a vacation. Mother and I accepted an invitation from Jock and Eva to visit with them in their new home at the Curtiss Candy Farm at Cary, Illinois, which was about fifty miles out of Chicago. I had the opportunity of seeing this new farm that was to be a great show place. I was not disappointed. The farm was situated in a picturesque region overlooking scenic Fox River valley, a famous resort spot for Chicagoans. Otto Schnering, president of the Curtiss products, purchased the farm near Cary from the multimillionaire owner of the Yellow Cab Company in Chicago, a Mr. Hertz, who used the place for a horse farm, with stables, amphitheater, and race track. The many acres of beautiful woodland afforded pleasant excursions and many scenic thrills for the guests that flocked to this place. The original owner of the property had sent his architects abroad for the plans of the main building, which was built in French and English pattern. After Mr. Schnering had purchased the farmstead, he spent additional millions to convert it into a show place for his favorite purebred Guernsey and Holstein cows. His favorite Guernsey was the $17,000 Quail Roost Primrose cow, and among his Holstein favorites were Abegwait Sparkee and Dunloggin Adeen, two of the breed's grand old matrons. I was told that Mr. Schnering never leaves this farm, but spends his time with his cows and his large flower gardens that are miracles of color delight. The name "Curtiss," used for the many products made by the company, was Mr. Schnering's mother's maiden name. Jock told me that the screen actress, Myrna Loy, who was once married to a son of the former owner, had spent some time living on that same farm.

More than a hundred men were continually at work on this one farm alone, with painters and carpenters on a year-round payroll. The stupendous immensity of the organization was staggering. Jock and his family lived in a lovely home that comprised one corner of the largest building on the farm, which looked more like a giant entertainment pavilion than a cow barn. Jock could walk from his house directly into the barn, which had two hundred box stalls arranged in a quadrangle opening into a large court in the center. The stalls themselves were finished in white enamel, and were kept immaculately clean by two people who had nothing else to do. The purpose was to keep these barns as spotless as the Curtiss candy kitchens in Chicago. Fluorescent lights gleamed above each box stall as well as tiny ultraviolet ray lamps to kill bacteria. A new barn for maternity pens was being built on the farm. This was to be the last word in elegance. Airconditioned throughout, the pens were being made with two-tone tile with glass brick windows.

Jock showed me the spacious auditorium that joined the main building. Carpenters were at work then refinishing it.

"The Curtiss people are getting it ready for the first in a series of annual sales they're going to hold here. The sales will be known as the Curtiss Candy Classic Sales. The first one will be in June, 1946. You'd better have something pretty good to bring to this sale, Mel. They're going to try to make it the highest averaging sale in the history of the breed."

After a thoroughly satisfying visit, we returned to Newton, arriving home early in the morning. Some of the men were just going to breakfast when I arrived at the farm. I asked them the question that was uppermost in my thoughts, "How's Amy?"

"She died while you were away," they replied.

I thought they were joking. "Why, you're kidding me, aren't you?"

Mel Campbell came up to the group at that moment, and confirmed their statement. I walked into the office with him, while he explained how it had happened. "The day after you left, Amy came in from the pasture in great pain. We called the veterinarian at once. He informed us she had a twisted intestine. I wanted to take her to the clinic at Ames, but he assured me it would be of no use. Amy died shortly after. I could've called you back, but there was nothing you could've done for her, and I didn't want to spoil your vacation. Really, Mel, I'd rather have lost any other cow in the herd, knowing how much you thought of her."

"I know everything possible was done for her," I said appreciatively. "She was right in the middle of a great 2x record."

"Yes, I know she was," Mel confirmed. "She was a remarkable heifer. Perhaps we can get her dam back."

We found that Amy's mother was still alive in a herd near Sheffield, and we were able to buy her. Princess was past ten years of age when she came to the Maytag Dairy Farm, but she did not look more than six or seven. She attracted a great deal of attention because of her splendid type. She was a rare cow to own, not only because of her own very good production with high test and pleasing type, but more because of the ability she demonstrated to transmit all of these superior qualities to her daughters. We did not run the old matron on test that year, but I decided that if she freshened all right the next year she might be given another chance. She had several good records on twice-a-day milking, but had never had a chance on official test.

Not a day passed but that I learned some new thing. I was beginning to realize that there was no limit to the knowledge to be learned from the study of dairy cows. Mel Campbell taught me the technique of artificial insemination of cows, and during the winter, he suggested that I attend the Graham Scientific Breeding School at St. Paul, Minnesota, at the farm's expense. I was elated at the chance I had long wished for. There I received among other things a thorough working knowledge of the reproductive organs of the cow. I learned from Dr. Graham, who is not only a keen psychologist but a practical cowman as well, that the best methods in caring for dairy cows, both when they are sick and when they are well, are those which follow as closely as possible the laws of nature.

Later, while attending a lecture in Newton, I met another man who gave me much useful information about udders and milking. This man was Dr. W. E. Petersen of the University of Minnesota. By his experiments with a cowless udder that functioned normally and produced real milk, this man learned secrets about the miracle of milk secretion no man had ever known before. The system of fast and complete milking that I had learned so well from my good friend, Paul Behn, at Rose Harbor Holstein Farm, was exactly the one recommended by Professor Petersen.

At last I felt more sure of myself, felt that I could now answer some of the questions that daily confronted me, instead of always searching for explanations.

☆ XVII ☆

Changes at Maytags

THE POLICIES that had been in operation at Maytag Dairy Farms for so many years under the able supervision of Jock McCormack were for the most part carefully adhered to after his departure. It takes years of study and planning to put a herd of purebred dairy cattle into successful operation. When such a plan has been found to be practicable after twenty-five years of fruitful effort, it is best to continue that system with as few changes as possible for the good of the herd. Now to make a really worth-while contribution to the

152

breed, a herd must proceed steadily toward a well-conceived ideal. Nothing can destroy that achievement more quickly than a radical change of management every few years. A herd does not establish a bloodline of its own in one generation of cows; it requires a generation of man!

Through my efforts, two important renovations were instituted at the farm. They were, however, the result of tendencies being demanded by the breed as a whole rather than by any personal predilection. Just as the earlier seven-day records had been found inadequate and were cast aside, so had four-time milking slowly become less popular. Breeders were becoming more intelligent in regard to these glamour records. They were discovering that bulls out of these 1,000-pound-fat cows whose records were made on 4x often lowered the production in their own 400-pound 2x herds when used in them. The war hastened the change from 4x milking to less frequent milkings. Countless great breeders throughout the country were forced to disperse their herds. Others could no longer obtain the necessary help to continue milking three and four times a day. The natural effect was the growing disfavor of 4x milking. Carnation and Maytag were about the only two great herds in the country that tenaciously held to this grand old tradition. Then came the time when Carnation, owner of more world champion milk and butterfat producers than any other herd in the world regardless of breed, started a string of cows on 3x milking, retaining but a single string on 4x. It was only a matter of time when Maytags would follow their example. It was difficult to sacrifice a tradition that had stood for twenty-five years.

The 4x milking division was discontinued in 1953, and no more records will be made of this milking frequency. The deathblow to 4x milking came dramatically when the Carnation cow, Carnation Homestead Daisy Madcap, became the first cow in the world of any breed to produce over 1,500 pounds of fat in a year — and this on 3x. The irony of it was that this same cow also held the world's record on 4x with 1,413 pounds fat.

Mel Campbell had spoken to me several times about the matter, endeavoring to sound out my reaction to the idea. I had always been an advocate of 3x milking for several reasons; but, because I was not sure how it would work out in actual practice, I would not make an out-and-out appeal for the change. When asked for my opinion, however, I offered the points in favor of the change as I saw them.

"I believe a record on 3x milking is more truly an indication of a cow's ability than one made on either 2x or 4x milking," I told Mel. "Four-time milking is the acid test of a cow's constitutional ability. She is forced to the point where her life may be shortened by many years, and that is not what we are working for in our dairy herds. When we find a great brood cow, we want to get as many offspring from her as we possibly can. Twice-a-day milking, on the other hand, does not give the unusually high producer a chance to show what she can actually do. Then, too, milking her three times a day instead of twice a day will tend to keep her udder from breaking away, for some cows produce too much milk for the good of their udders when milked only twice a day."

"I've felt all along that the time would come when we would just naturally be swept along with the 3x trend," Mr. Campbell said, "but I hate to think of the reduction of about 20 per cent in milk if we make the change. That's about the loss I've figured we should have to take if we changed to 3x milking. That's the reason also I've been reluctant to give you the go ahead signal."

"That's my reason, too, for not pressing the matter with you," I answered, "for I'd feel rather silly if I told you that there would be no reduction when we made the change, and then found out for myself that my theory was entirely wrong."

"And your theory, then," Mel asked, "is that you actually believe we will not take a loss in milk if we turn over from 4x to 3x milking?"

"Exactly," I returned. "Naturally, the cows that are now being milked only twice a day will, when they are milked three times and fed an additional feeding with more regular hours than they've been milked, respond with an increased amount of milk. The test cows, on the other hand, will not drop much if any when the change is made."

"But what reason have you for believing that the 4x cows will not drop?" Mel asked incredulously. "I've always been of the opinion that cows will milk heavier the more times a day they're milked."

"Cows are not all alike," I explained, "and there may be a few that'll milk more on 4x milking than on less frequent milkings. They would probably be those very rare cows that milk up to and over a hundred pounds of milk a day. Realizing that milk secretion slows up only when pressure is built in the udder, I can see no reason for milking more often than is required to relieve the udder when it is full.

Specifically, if a cow produces less than fifty pounds of milk a day, and her udder can easily hold twenty-five pounds, she should not have to be milked more than twice a day. This is not the only explanation of my theory. The most important one is the fact that pressure inside the udder, or the desire of the cow to get relief, is a most important factor in the complex process of letting down her milk. The more often a cow is milked, the less likely she is to respond to a complete letdown of milk. I have discovered very few cows that completely let their milk down when milked every six hours. And going back to the milk secretion process, we know that if milk is left in the udder from one milking to another, the cow will gradually dry herself up. Therefore I believe that a cow will hold out more persistently throughout her lactation if she's milked three times a day. This is only my theory. I believe I'm right, yet I can't promise you it'll work out in actuality because I've never tested it out."

"I'm just confident enough in you, Mel," the manager said, "to believe you. You have my permission to make the change-over at any time you wish. I should like to see your schedule of work outlined for milking and feeding when you have it finished, to see how it will tie in with the meal planning in the boarding house, the handling of the milk and equipment in the creamery, and the availability of milk for our deliveries."

In my years of work at Maytag Dairy Farms, I found Mr. Campbell always fully cooperative as he was in the incident just related. He trusted completely those he placed in responsible positions, and gave them entire authority to handle the affairs in their respective positions as they saw fit. This encouraged them to do their best for the animals in their charge.

There were many consignment sales of national importance in which an establishment of such repute as Maytags naturally felt itself obliged to participate. To select the right animals for a consignment sale was always a difficult decision to make. For advertising purposes it was necessary to select some of our best animals to send to these sales, and at the same time to refrain from sacrificing certain individuals that were essential to our breeding program. Mel Campbell always considered my opinion before letting an animal go from the herd. Art Peterson, one of the nation's top sale managers, noticed this kind deference shown to me by Mr. Campbell, and once made this remark:

"In all the herds I have visited throughout the country I know of none other where the manager has placed such decisions in the hands of his herdsman."

On January 1, 1946, everything was in readiness to make the change to 3x milking. From the very first it was popular both with the men and with the cows. More than half of the cows that were on 4x milking surprised even me by producing more milk after the change had been made. Mel Campbell was both greatly relieved and well pleased to see the change working so smoothly. The greatest benefits and proof of its merit, however, were yet to demonstrate themselves.

The other change made at the farm was in the matter of earlier breeding after freshening. The policy had been to wait for five months following calving before a cow was bred back. It often happened that cows failed to conceive sometimes for several months after that, so that many of them were dry for long periods of time. This tendency was widespread in our better herds. The mistaken notion was that for large records a cow should remain open during most of the first half of her lactation. Some people feel that a cow does not milk so well at the latter part of her lactation if she is caring for a fetus, and believe further that part of her record has to be sacrificed to raise this calf. The Holstein public did not think very much about this at first, but within the last few years there has been a growing demand for records that qualify for the ten-months' division. This is a healthy attitude and shows that breeders are awakening to the merits of the cow that can make good records year after year throughout a long life, and drop a calf about once a year.

I brought this subject to the attention of the management shortly after I was placed in charge of the herd. Again Mr. Campbell was very cooperative.

"I believe you have something there," he said, "and both Jock and I have discussed the same issue many times before, but did nothing about it. I must confess that I've been a little lax about the matter myself."

"It wasn't so important in the days when the herd was run as a hobby, and the main concern was to obtain big records," I continued, "but when a herd is on its own, it can't afford to lose the number of calves that it would have if cows were rebred three months after calving instead of five, to say nothing of the amount of milk that's lost when the cows remain dry so long."

"Do you think that every cow should be bred three months after freshening?" Mel asked.

"Every cow that is not on test should be bred three months after calving, provided she has cleared up properly," I answered. "Cows on test should be bred at four months, and in very rare cases where a cow might be making a sensational record one might wait as long as five months with her, and if she conceives at the first service she could still qualify. But this would be only in rare cases. The benefits from such a program are many. In the first place there'd be more milk and more calves. Most of the breeding troubles that plague our large herds would be automatically overcome by earlier breeding. It is a well-known fact that the longer one waits before breeding a cow the more difficult it becomes to get her with calf. What good is a big record if the cow does not have any more offspring to cash in on that record? It has been said that the cow that's allowed to remain open for long periods of time doesn't live so long as the cow that has a calf every year. Be that as it may, the cow that calves regularly has a longer useful life than the cow that has a calf every two years."

Mel Campbell was not born in Scotland, but you could always expect a Scottish argument. It came here again.

"How much milk will we lose in one lactation by breeding her back so soon?" he asked.

"I've found that cows that have calves every year and breed regularly produce much better year after year than those that are dry for months and months."

This was a convincing argument, if true. Everyone has seen cows that have been dry perhaps for as long as a year or more. They have been rolling in fat for as long a time, and the owner jubilantly expects such animals to "go great guns" when they freshen; but he finds that after they calve they do not milk off the fat that has accumulated on their backs over a period of several months. This fact explains why so many of our over-fitted show animals do not develop into good producers, and why the better judges are now recognizing this fact and are frowning upon the practice of over-fitting.

☆ XVIII ☆

Maytag Ormsby Fobes Olive

ON AUGUST 18, 1944, a heifer calf was born at the Maytag Dairy Farms. There was nothing in her breeding to indicate that she would be any different from the dozens of other heifer calves born every year at the farm, but as the weeks passed, she showed promise of being a very flashy youngster. Her early life was no different from that of the other heifers her own age. Because of her later development and accomplishments, we shall follow briefly the routine of her life to show how the young stock at Maytags get their upbringing.

The little heifer calf was officially christened as Maytag Ormsby Fobes Olive. The student of breeding would be interested in her parentage. She was the result of two inbreds of entirely opposite strains, much like an ear of hybrid corn. Her sire, Maytag Ormsby Fobes, was line-bred for generations in the Ormsby family that Maytags had intensified; her dam was Olive Montvic Piebe, a purchased cow that carried several crosses of Mount Victoria breeding. The dam was, therefore, a complete outcross; but she brought just what was needed into a well-established strain to give it vigor and constitution. It was with this purpose in mind that Maytags purchased, shortly after this time, a son of Wisconsin Admiral Burke Lad, the sire that was exerting a tremendous influence throughout the United States. By bringing this son of Burke into the Maytag herd, we were not, however, introducing blood that was entirely foreign to our bloodline, but rather, we hoped, enough new blood to rejuvenate our closely bred animals.

Little Olive was mostly black, in contrast to her dam who had more white than black, but she did have a white switch and the white legs necessary to be registered. For three or four days she nursed her mammy, making a veritable pig of herself on the colostrum that was the first product manufactured in her dam's udder. Nothing known to man could take the place of this first milk to give the young calf the proper start in life. Colostrum more nearly approaches the chemical substances of blood than does milk, and contains antibodies that protect the young calf against diseases.

After the first few days, the old cow was taken into the milking barn, there to go on test. Meanwhile, the little calf was getting its first automobile ride in a pickup, which took it across the road to the nurse cow barn, where little Olive was put in a pen together with three other calves her own age. There was a big black cow in the pen, but she didn't smell just right; so Olive refused to go near her. She watched her three little friends drink from the old udder; when her own stomach ached with hunger, she bawled as loudly as she could. When it seemed she was going to die and nobody would care, a man came into the pen and noticed her plight. It was the same man she had seen when she first saw the light of day. She was not afraid of him, and tried to suck his fingers.

The man shut off the other three calves in one corner of the pen with some bales of straw, so Olive could get acquainted with her new mammy. He pushed her up to the old cow and placed one of the teats in her mouth. Olive took a few sips, and realizing it tasted almost like her own mother's milk, she sucked until her little sides almost split wide open. The old cow turned around once to sniff her, but turned back to her hay, quite used to the idea of mothering every Bessie's, Flossie's, and Gertie's youngsters. After a few meals like this, the other three calves were turned loose again in the pen with Olive, and she had to push and shove to get her share of the milk.

One of the first days, Olive had her picture taken. Then she was put back in her pen with her foster mother and sisters, but she could not figure out why that good man tortured her so. First, he cut some hair off two little circles on her head and put on something that for a time seemed to drive her crazy. How was she to know that he was applying caustic to kill the little horn buttons, so she would not have to have them cut off when they grew bigger and would bleed and leave deep holes in her head? She knew only that the horrid stuff burned, burned so badly that it was giving her a headache, and she took her back leg and tried to rub the headache. Her little foot would not go where she wanted it to, and she fell down hard on the ground, where she lay for a time, shaking her head. While she was figuring out some new way to get rid of her headache, the man stuck her neck with a sharp needle. That did it. She got up and ran around the pen, trying to find a way out. She didn't know that she was being vaccinated for hemorrhagic septicemia. After that the man caught her and made her lie down in the straw, while he examined her udder for supernumerary teats. It was a good thing for her that she didn't have any extra ones, or they would have been snipped off in a hurry. All in all it had been a bad day, and no wonder she didn't feel like drinking any supper.

When she was about two weeks old, Olive began nibbling some grain and calf pellets in a feed manger in one corner of the pen, and she reached her long neck up through the slits in the hay rack and pulled out some green upland hay. She chewed some of it, but most of it she just pulled out and let fall on the ground. That was more fun at first than eating it, but when she grew a little and her friends grew a little, and there wasn't enough milk at the fountain to satisfy her, she learned that the hay filled her up. It made her thirsty, too, and she took a few sips out of a bucket of fresh water the man had placed in one end of the pen. It was cool, while the drink from the

INKA RUE OLLIE POSCH

MAYTAG ORMSBY FOBES OLIVE

ALL-TIME ALL-AMERICAN GET OF MAN-O-WAR

No Other Get Ever Won All-American Honors Four Different Years

fountain was warm. She couldn't understand this; but the water tasted good, and she drank and drank.

The weeks passed, and the little heifer grew faster than the other three calves in the same pen. When she was about two months old, a man came into her pen one day with a rope, and put it around her neck. She didn't like it at all, and ran away as fast as she could. But when she got so far, the rope stopped her, and she landed ker-plunk on her side. For a minute the wind was knocked out of her. But only for a moment, then she was up and away again. She could go only so far, and the rope would stop her. In this way, she was led across the road again to the large calf barn. This was her first lesson in leading, and she didn't like it a bit. In the big calf barn, she was put in a pen with two other heifers her size, and there she was left to get acquainted as best she could.

The next taste she had of milk was out of a pail. It was not so good as out of the fountain. The cream had been removed, of course. But since she was a little pig, and she could drink it faster this way, Olive liked that. The man didn't give her nearly as much as she wanted. She didn't know that too much milk was worse than not enough. There was a little ground feed to eat, with something new on top. It was beet pulp, and it tasted good. There was all the hay she could eat to develop her digestive system, which would be called upon later to perform some rather amazing feats. Olive didn't understand that even with the best breeding in the world, she couldn't develop the fullest use of her inherited ability without the proper feed and care, or that the first year of her life was the most important one of all.

More than anything else in the world, Olive loved to eat, and she grew faster than any of the animals that were put with her. When she was about six months old, she felt the sting of the needle again. This time it was a vaccination against Bangs disease. In May, she was nine months old and graduated from the calf barn into the heifer lot on the hill. Here she raced through the grass with the other heifers, outrunning, outclassing them all. She had all the grass she could eat, and some hay, with a little grain once a day. When she was thirsty, there was water to drink from a tank under the shade trees.

After the summer had passed and the grass was covered with snow, she could run into the large heifer barn for protection from the cold and wind. The south doors were always left open so she could go outside whenever she wanted to. During the winter, she received a little silage with her hay and grain. She was not allowed to get fat, because she was not yet with calf. She was not pampered, but allowed to "rough it." When she was a year and a half of age, she was bred artificially, and in three months time she was examined and found to be safe with calf. Still she was not heavily fed with grain. Still she remained in the open heifer barn where she had complete freedom to go in and out.

About two months before Olive was due to calve, she was taken into the maternity barn for special feeding and care. Her days of freedom were over. Her useful life was about to begin. In the maternity barn, she was handled often by the men who worked with her. Though Olive was always gentle, she showed a strong spirit. She would be no problem when she went into the milking barn because she would be used to being handled. She was rapidly putting on fat for the time when she would need this reserve flesh. Every day she was allowed to walk out into the lot for exercise. This was very important for the pregnant heifer. Exercise makes calving easier, and lessens the danger of troubles following calving.

This was the way that Olive was cared for as a heifer. This was the method followed with every heifer that was born in the Maytag herd. This particular heifer was destined to be perhaps the most outstanding one ever bred at the Maytag Farms for show type and production combined. That she went on to make over 600 pounds of butterfat on 3x at two years of age (qualifying for the ten-months' division), even while she was making a wide circuit of fairs that took her to Toronto, Canada, and then to win All-American honors for three years in succession, is now history; and the end of her story is still in the unwritten years ahead.

But we leave our Olive heifer at this point in her life where she was taken into the maternity barn, and we shall proceed from this point in the life of a dairy female to another cow that was about to freshen in the test barn. She was to be the recipient of all the applied knowledge learned by the herdsman at Maytag Dairy Farms, from all his years of experience. That cow was Inka Rue Ollie Posch!

☆ XIX ☆

Inka Rue Ollie Posch

INKA RUE OLLIE POSCH did not go to the maternity barn as did every other female in the herd when she was ready to calve. Instead, "Inkie" remained in her own box stall in the main test barn, a stall she had occupied ever since she had her first calf several years before. Every year she had been run on official test, and had kept her own box stall year in and year out. Here she remained even during her dry periods. She had always been a favorite at the farm, and had turned out a great record every year. Another reason why she was privileged to keep her own box stall was the fact that Inkie was an exceptionally large animal, weighing over a ton. She was rather slow and awkward in her movements, and did not get along very well with the younger cows and heifers in the other pastures.

Inkie was due to calve again the last week in February, 1946. When I announced that I was going to put her on test again in Class B (3x milking) and make a thousand-pound-fat record on her, no one took me very seriously. The old matron was coming on nine years of age now, they argued, which is past the prime of bovine life. Besides, had she not been handled previously by one of the country's acknowledged wizards as a test cow milker, and her highest record so far was 987 pounds of fat? This was made in Class A (4x milking). It was then believed that cows would produce more the oftener they were milked. Even Mel Campbell said that if Inkie could not make a thousand-pound record on 4x, she certainly could not make it on 3x milking. Furthermore, this cow had been milked four times a day for five lactations. Feeding and milking a cow every six hours is a terrific strain on her, and Inkie had withstood this grueling test for five years.

Even Jock, who had more faith in her than anyone else, shook his head when she finished her 987-pound-fat record, and remarked, "There goes her last chance for a thousand-pound-fat record."

But I had waited years for just this chance, and I was not going to give it up. I saw in this cow a greater possibility for achieving my ambition than in any other cow I had ever seen. Every cowman dreams of making a thousand-pound-fat record. It is one of the hardest things to accomplish. It was the one goal I had not reached.

Inkie had been put dry in November, 1945, and I immediately took over personal charge of her. She received about eighteen pounds of 14 per cent protein ration every day. The percentage of protein was never increased during her subsequent lactation. Usual test cow rations contain as much as 18 per cent protein and higher. High amounts of concentrated protein tend to burn out a cow. The number of pounds of grain is mentioned merely as a fact in this particular case, not as a hard-and-fast rule. There are too many factors involved in feeding grain to dairy cows to present any specific rule to follow in the matter. Such considerations include the amount of milk a cow is producing, the percentage of butterfat in her milk, the stage of development of the fetus she is carrying, if any, and the condition of her own flesh. The only correct way to arrive at the amount of grain to feed a dairy cow is to make a careful study of each cow's own needs and to feed each cow individually. A good feeder watches each cow's appetite, her bowel movements, her udder, and her feed manger. She should wash her own dishes at each feeding, like any good house-keeper.

With her grain Inkie received half a bucket of soaked beet pulp with a liberal amount of blackstrap molasses mixed with it. A small feed-ing of silage was given her once a day. She was fed all the hay she could clean up twice a day. The very best hay obtainable was selected for this cow — hay that was fine-stemmed, leafy, bright green, and sweet. Both alfalfa and clover hay were fed. Although alfalfa hay is the best for dairy cows, it is a known fact that they will do better if alfalfa is supplemented with some other kind of hay. It was most important that she be fed the highest quality hay during her dry period when she was building up her system for the tremendous job she was about to perform. Dairymen frequently forget these vital facts: the time to feed liberally is during the dry period, and if a cow is to be skimped, it is better to skimp after she is producing. The reverse is more often the case.

My first thought was to win the old cow over. She must learn to like me, and to look forward to my visits to her pen, for the man who works with a cow has more to do with the amount of milk a cow produces than the feed that is given to her. I recognized this funda-mental rule, and proceeded to spend as much of my extra time as I could with the old cow. When I had nothing else to do, I would brush her. I doubt if there is anything a cow loves better except to be fed.

At first she would shake her head at me whenever I tried to pet her, but she soon got over that. A cow has a most peculiar way of distin-guishing her friends from her enemies, as instinctive and as enigmatic as the way a child has. Some say she can smell fear, enmity, or affec-tion in people; I am inclined, however, to believe that she has other instincts besides her keen olfactory sense that prompt her to trust so quickly the person who loves her.

The fact remains that this great cow had a complete change of dis-position. She was soon to be seen with her head high over the box stall, her eyes wide and searching for her master to come into the barn. When she caught sight of him, she would toss her head up and down impatiently.

A good dairy cow puts on flesh rapidly during her dry period.

Inkie was such a cow. By early February, she was in excellent condition, but not overly fat. Although Inkie was not a show cow in any sense of the word, she was every inch a real dairy animal. Despite her tremendous size, there was great dairy refinement written all over her. Even when she was carrying much flesh, her shoulders were smooth and wedge-shaped, the vertebrae were clearly defined. She had a very deep barrel with a wide spring of rib, indicative of her astounding digestive capacity. Her tail was long and very thin, a good sign of a high-producing cow. Her legs, set far apart, were straight and strong. She had a capacious udder which might not have been just what the show boys wanted; yet it was a marvelous working udder, pliable, and still well attached after more than fifty tons of milk had passed through it. The two large milk veins that ran up both sides of her belly were crooked and as large as a man's wrist. In addition to these two milk veins that are normally to be found on every milk cow, Inkie had a third umbilical milk vein running up the center of her belly, a little something extra found only in cows of rare producing ability. Inkie's head was outstanding. Though she was rightfully criticised for possessing a Roman nose and for allowing her ears to droop pitifully down over her cheeks, she did have a strong head, a broad muzzle with large open nostrils and a strong clean jaw, breed characteristics which substantiated the fact that she was a good feeder. This latter quality is perhaps the most important one to look for in a test cow, for without it a cow can never hope to make a great record, no matter how well she is bred. It was Inkie's full bright eyes, however, that reminded me most of my long-lost pet. One of them had a provoking way of showing a wide band of white when she turned her head sideways to look at me.

By the middle of February, Inkie was beginning to make up an udder; to prevent undue congestion all aggravating foods such as corn and silage were taken away from her. Bran, oats, molasses, beet pulp, and high-quality hay, all laxative foods, comprised her diet.

While she is waiting for those last days to elapse before calving, let us examine briefly her interesting pedigree.

As previously stated, the Maytag herd was founded on the blood of Sir Pietertje Ormsby Mercedes 37th, conceded to be the greatest Holstein sire that ever lived. He was discovered in the herd of John Erickson, a farmer-breeder in Wisconsin. This bull brought sudden, national fame to this small, unknown Holstein breeder. When his herd was dispersed in 1924, new price figures for the breed were made. Maytags purchased five females at this dispersal, outstanding among them being an own daughter of 37th, Princess de Ormsby. Shortly after this, Sir Inka May came into the limelight as the All-American Junior Yearling son of May Walker Ollie Homestead, holder of the United States fat record at that time. Carnation Farms had just purchased this great young sire from the Minnesota Holstein Company of Austin, Minnesota.

E. H. Maytag drove to Austin with the avowed purpose of breeding Princess de Ormsby to Sir Inka May, with the hope of getting a bull calf for a future Maytag herd sire. When he drove into the yard of the Minnesota farm, he was met by Vere Culver, manager of the establishment. Mrs. Maytag was asked into the house to visit with Mrs. Culver, while the men discussed the business at hand.

"I'm sorry, Mr. Maytag," Vere Culver said when he learned the nature of Mr. Maytag's visit, "but the services of Sir Inka May are not for sale. He's been sold to the Carnation Milk Farms, and while he's waiting shipment out to Seattle, it is understood that outside services to him are no longer available. But come on out to the barn and I'll show you the bull anyway."

The two men went on to the barn and saw the bull and the rest of the herd. After their inspection was over, they returned to the house, where they found the two women discussing washing machines.

"I was just telling your wife," Mrs. Culver said to Mr. Maytag as he came into the room, "that I've been wanting a Maytag Washer and haven't been able to get one."

Elmer Maytag began bartering then and there. "I'll tell you what I'll do, Mrs. Culver. If you can persuade Vere to let me breed my 37th daughter to Sir Inka May I'll send you a washing machine."

"What do you say, Vere?" Mrs. Culver coaxed.

"Oh, all right, you win," he said laughingly. "Bring your cow, E. H."

That was before artificial insemination had become known; so Princess de Ormsby had to be trucked from Newton to Austin, where she was bred to Sir Inka May, just before he went to Carnations. Princess de Ormsby had a bull calf from this mating, marked just like the true type model, and Mr. Maytag was the proudest man in the world. The animal was thereafter dubbed the washing machine bull, and was recorded as Prince Ormsby Inka May. Later, he was bred back to his own dam, and the cow, Princess de Ormsby 4th, was born. This inbred cow was tested on several different occasions, but did not produce nearly so well as had been expected. Finally, she was sent to the butchers as a hopeless case, but only after she had left two sons behind her. In time, both of these sons proved out remarkably well, demonstrating the point that an inbred animal may not show a high degree of production herself, but is capable of transmitting high levels of production to her offspring if she has those latent genes in her own make-up. The greatest of these sons of Princess de Ormsby 4th was Sir Posch Ormsby Inka, one of the highest index sires in the United States in 1937 — and also the sire of Inka Rue Ollie Posch.

A few days before Inkie was ready to calve, she received daily intravenous injections of calcium gluconate. She could be depended upon to have an attack of milk fever at every freshening, and this method of giving her shots for milk fever before calving was not meant to prevent the disease, because it would not. But it would lighten the attack when it came, and keep her from going down.

On the twenty-sixth day of February, it appeared that the cow was ready to calve. Her box stall, therefore, was immaculately cleaned and disinfected, and the floor heavily limed. Then it was bedded deeply with bright, dry straw. Everything was now ready for the great event.

The day passed slowly, and night came, but no calf. By all indications, Inkie should have started laboring. I was getting anxious, and kept constant vigil over her. When midnight came and still no calf, I decided to make an examination to see if the calf was still alive and to determine if the cervix was distended for delivery. Examination showed that the calf was alive and ready for delivery, but for some reason was not forthcoming. That reason was now obvious: parturient paralysis had already set in and the cow could not deliver the calf. I called my assistant and another man and proceeded to take the calf from the cow. The calf was very large, and with no help from the cow, the operation was rather difficult.

In due time the calf was delivered, a big black bull, and very much alive — a calf that was later named Maytag Dean Deluxe and used in the Maytag herd. On account of the condition of the cow, no milk would dare be drawn from the udder. Consequently, the calf was taken away from its mother at once. Then, attention was promptly given to the old cow. Warm water and a hot bran mash were given, which Inkie took readily. She was blanketed, given another shot for milk fever, and then allowed to rest for the remainder of the night.

Inkie did not go down with milk fever, but responded to treatment very well. She did not lose her appetite, in spite of the fact that the touch of paralysis had caused her to retain the afterbirth. She recovered slowly from this setback, and was put on official test the fourth day after calving, according to the regulations of Advanced Registry tests.

The total for the three milkings of her first day on test was 42.8 pounds of milk. Another cow that had freshened at about the same time as Inkie had was milking over ninety pounds a day with the milking machine, while I was milking Inkie by hand. My assistant enjoyed joshing me about this.

"You'd better give up on the old girl," he would say, "and take over Lass. She'll beat your Inkie all to smithereens."

"That's all right, Bob," I tossed back lightly, "Lass will need all the head start she can get."

Inkie milked about sixty pounds a day during the first week, slid into the seventies for the second and third weeks on test, and by the end of March was milking in the eighties. I was taking her easy yet, and was glad to see her gaining slowly but steadily.

Spring came early that year, and by the end of March the grass was tall enough in the little yard south of the barn in the valley so that Inkie could get a good fill. Blue grass is best grazed before it gets tough and heads out; with legumes, which grow from buds on the crowns instead of by lengthening of the lower parts of the stems and blades as do the grasses, it is best to let them obtain a greater growth before pasturing them.

The rich salts and minerals in the young grass did Inkie a world of good. She was always impatient to be turned out into the grassy plot each morning after being milked, and would stroll down along the little stream where the grass was greenest and tallest. The large pastures on the hill were not nearly so far along, and could not be grazed for some time. Since there was only a limited quantity of grass in the yard by the buildings, Inkie was the only cow that was turned out here. In this way, she had plenty to eat. On the ninth day of April, she reached ninety pounds of milk, and on the twelfth day she had ninety-nine pounds.

On the morning of the thirteenth, she gave 36.3 pounds of milk, her highest single milking so far. I was almost certain that she would reach a hundred pounds that day. She had never quite made that mark at any time during her life, even back in the days when she was milked four times a day. I turned her out in the lot as usual, and went on about my morning's work. She was constantly on my mind, and every now and then I would glance down into the ravine to watch her as she ate grass, oblivious to everything else.

Once I looked down and could not see her. I decided to have a run down to see where she had disappeared. I did not find her until I reached the bank of the stream. She was standing in the water, looking up at me with a blank expression on her face. I wondered how she had got down the bank and into the water, but concluded she had found a spot where the incline was not so steep and had gone down to get a drink. I went back to the barn without disturbing her, but the more I thought about it the more puzzled I became.

I kept thinking about her as I worked. Finally, I became alarmed and decided to go back down, and if she was still in the water, I would drive her up on the bank.

When I came to the spot where I had left her, I glanced downstream and saw that she had followed the creek and had walked under the bridge over which the cows had to pass to get to the pasture. Inkie was mud from head to foot. How she had got this way, I could not tell. But I realized she had not gone down to the water for a drink, that she had grazed too close to the edge of the bank, and the soft dirt had given way beneath her great weight, causing her to slide down the bank.

"Come on out, Inkie," I called to her.

She knew what I meant, and started up the bank. I was sure she was going to make it. Then, all at once, the great weight went to her rear quarters, and her hind legs sank slowly into the soft spongy mud. She could not budge them. Slowly, she rolled back down the steep grade and sank, floundering, into the icy water.

In a matter of minutes the entire barn crew together with the farm gang were on the scene with tractors, ropes, and chains to rescue Inkie from the cold mire. Bill Kendall, our trucker, was an expert at knot tying.

"Take over, Bill," I told him. "I'm too excited to think clearly anyway."

"Shall we try pulling her out by the neck?" he inquired.

"We can try that," I answered, "and maybe when we start pulling she'll help some."

"Won't that break her neck?" someone asked.

"They can stand a lot of pull on their necks," the farm foreman told us.

The stout ropes were tied around the cow's neck with a bowline knot that would not tighten about the neck and choke the cow when the tractor started moving.

"Okay, take her away," Bill shouted to the tractor man. "Take her easy."

Slowly the rope tightened. The neck stretched further . . . further . . . Inkie did not move, did not try. Her massive body wedged deeper in the side of the bank.

"Hold her!" I cried, frantically waving my arms at the driver. "Her neck'll break."

Ordinarily this is the way animals are rescued from such places, but in this case the size of the cow, the steep grade of the bank, and the animal's complete helplessness prevented the success of such a method.

"We'll have to get her onto something," Bill said. "Bring that gate over here, men!"

The heavy wooden gate was brought and placed as far under the cow as possible.

"Now everyone lift and see if we can slide her rear end around on the gate a little more," Bill commanded.

All the men applied themselves to this difficult task, and by pulling and straining, managed to heave her bulk onto the gate. The tractor started again. The gate moved a little, but the cow rolled to the side, and the boards of the gate shattered like small laths.

The gate was taken out of the water, and various other holds were tried. An hour or more had elapsed, and the cow was still as deep in the muddy, cold water as she had been.

I was becoming desperately alarmed by this time. I had almost given up any hopes for the record she had begun when I first saw her sink into the mud; now I realized that her life was in jeopardy.

I tried to reason calmly. The rest of the men were just about at their wit's end. Then I thought of another plan.

"Why not tie ropes to all four legs, and pull her straight out?" I suggested. "I'll stand to one side and hold her udder up so it won't pull under her."

"That might work all right," Bill answered. "Let's try it."

Ropes were accordingly fastened around each leg and then secured to the tractor's drawbar, and the machine started pulling. One of the ropes was not pulling evenly and had to be tightened. The tractor moved ahead slowly again. The cow started moving, too. Easily, slowly the tractor moved away from the bank, the cow making the steep incline. Not once did Inkie move a muscle. Perhaps that saved her strength. Had she fought and struggled as was expected of her, it might not have helped to get her out any faster; and surely after she was pulled out, she would have been very weak. As it happened, when she reached the top of the bank, she lay there quietly and the warm rays of the April sun — nature's own kind doctor — administered to her.

I had thought before how I would take her directly to the barn, scrub her down with warm water, blanket her heavily, and bed her down deeply. I would massage her limbs to get the circulation started; I would work on her udder to try to prevent any serious trouble from this source. But after she had been pulled from the water, I realized how foolish it would be to try to get her to the barn — how impossible. Inkie could not have raised herself to her feet if she had tried. So I let her lie in the sun for a few hours while I made preparations for her in the barn.

It was well that this event happened during the warmest part of the day when the sun's beneficial rays shed their invigorating effects upon the universe. Shortly after noon, I walked back to the cow on the grassy bank. I would not have recognized her at any other time. I wondered if she could ever be cleaned again. Even her eyes were full of mud that had by now dried and caked on her. I patted her head encouragingly.

"Can you get up now, Inkie? Come on, old girl, try it. Try."

Inkie stumbled to her feet, stood there for a few minutes, and of her own accord started walking to the barn. I opened the barn door ahead of her. She walked inside and went directly to her own box stall. She began eating some hay I had put into her manger, and I brushed the dry mud out of her hair the best I could. It was surprising how much of it disappeared. I brought her some warm water, which she drank rather greedily. After she was blanketed, she sank down in the deep straw and rested heavily.

I did not get her up at milking time that afternoon. But after all the rest of the chores had been finished, I went back to her pen, and found that she had stood up of her own accord, and was busily eating hay again. I milked out twenty-five pounds of milk from her udder, then bathed it well with warm water containing epsom salts, dried it thoroughly and applied soothing, penetrating udder balm. Then I gently massaged the udder for at least half an hour.

At the midnight milking, Inkie had 43.1 pounds of milk, giving her a total production for the day of 104.4 pounds of milk, the first day in her life that she had topped the one-hundred-pound mark!

"We'll have to push her into the creek again," was Mel Campbell's witty comment the next morning.

Inkie seemed none the worse for her misadventure, and from that day she rose pound by pound: 108 . . . 112 . . . 113. How high would she go? Excitement became intense at the dairy over the remarkable feat this cow was performing.

In March she had made 4.23 pounds butterfat a day when the official tester was at the farm. Retests are not required the first month a cow is on test, but on the second month if a mature cow produces more than 3.3 pounds fat a day, a different tester is sent to the farm by the state college in charge of the test, and a retest is given the cow.

In April, Inkie made 4.35 pounds fat when the regular tester was at the farm, automatically making a retest necessary. Within a week another tester arrived, and ran a check test. On this official retest, Inkie produced 5.01 pounds fat a day, and milked up to 118.3 pounds of milk for the day, her peak day's milk production. This was equivalent to fifty-nine quarts of milk a day, containing approximately six pounds of butter.

In May she made another retest. For almost three months Inkie did not fall under the one-hundred-pound mark for one day. Four supervisors were employed during the conduct of this record.

Now I shall try to explain the significance of the tremendous job this cow was doing while milking up to 118 pounds of milk a day. To do this, I will follow in detail the happenings in just one of the 365 days that this cow was on test, for this process continued uninterruptedly for an entire year. Not one day did she rest, as a horse or even as a human being would have done.

Inkie was a regular factory for turning huge amounts of feed into milk. Few cows of the breed can equal her for these qualities. She was eating twenty-four pounds of grain each day, three buckets of soaked beet pulp with molasses, and all the good quality hay she would clean up. As a rule she remained in her box stall during the day, and was turned out to pasture at night. But that was entirely up to her. If she stood by the gate in her pen in the morning, letting me know she wanted outside, she was allowed to go out to pasture during the day when the weather was not too hot and the flies had not begun to be troublesome. If she did not care to walk outside when I opened her gate at night, or if the evening was especially sultry, Inkie was allowed to stay inside. In addition to all that she ate in the barn during the day, and the pasture she had during the night, I always had a full sack of freshly cut alfalfa that I had personally cut from the meadow each evening after my regular work was done. This method of cutting field-grown crops and feeding them directly to confined animals is known as soilage, and is practiced extensively by some of the large herds like Carnation Milk Farms. Inkie greedily devoured this green feed after the midnight milking.

It has been estimated that an average dairy cow makes about 41,000 jaw movements every day. A cow's mouth is wonderfully made to do this work. She has only a lower set of teeth in front for the purpose of cutting foods. The top or roof of the mouth is equipped with epidermal papillae (which look like rubber scalp massagers), which protect the deeper, softer structures and also probably assist in the retention of food in the mouth cavity. Much of the act of taking food into the mouth, or prehension as it is called, is accomplished by movements of the tongue.

The biggest job Inkie had was to regurgitate this gigantic mass during her rest periods. No wonder, then, that she had no time to sleep — for it is a queer fact that all cud chewing animals, including the cow, the sheep, goat, and camel, rest but never actually sleep. Very few cattlemen, and no other people at all, realize that the cow makes her milk lying down. For this reason, Inkie was never disturbed by anyone while on test during that year. Visitors were told why she could not be got up, and those who understood cattle appreciated our consideration for the cow and were not offended. Even when her pen was cleaned, Inkie was allowed to remain quiet; she became so used to having the men pull the manure from under her legs while she was lying down that she actually accommodated them by shifting and raising her own limbs. She knew almost to the minute when milking time had arrived. At those times she would be waiting for me with

her head high over the cast iron bars of her box stall, her eyes following me closely as I fed the rest of the cows.

Inkie was milked very regularly at 8 a.m., 4 p.m., and again at
midnight. The first act was the turning of the feed manger with its
grain and beet pulp so that the cow could eat. While she was performing this delightful task, I brushed her thoroughly. The importance of
grooming is manifold. Producing cleaner milk and giving the animal
a better appearance are the most obvious reasons for grooming a cow,
but they are not the most essential. Some dairymen claim a cow gives
more milk if she is brushed; I am inclined to believe that if she does,
it is because brushing tends to make the cow more attached to her
milker, and it is this deep personal affection which prompts her to
give more milk. As will be shown, a good milk cow works every bit
as hard as a horse does, without days off, but does not have sweat
glands as does a horse to keep her cool during the hot weather. Brushing gives an animal better circulation and tones up its system. How
many farmers insist upon currying their horses, but never think of
grooming their dairy cows!

After a vigorous massaging with a brush and curry comb, Inkie
was ready for the milking act. Her udder was very thoroughly and
gently massaged with a clean towel wrung out of very hot water, and
applied as warm as the human hand could stand. The floor of the
udder especially received this warm rubbing. The reason was not
particularly to get the udder clean, for it never was allowed to get
dirty; but rather to simulate the action of the calf with its warm
mouth rubbing against its mammy's udder. Here again the maternal
instinct, which is the key factor that governs all phases of successful
dairying, asserts itself. This rubbing and warmth is nature's way of
sending a message by the sensory nerves to the pituitary gland which
is situated at the base of the brain. The moment the message is received by this gland, a hormone is secreted into the blood stream. This
hormone, which is called oxytocin, rushes back to the udder and
starts the countless minute cells, called alveolae, to function in much
the same way that a tiny eye dropper squeezes out fluid. Thousands
of these tiny eye droppers inside the udder go to work at the request
of this hormone, and the milk starts pouring into the milk cistern.

The udder becomes distended in about a minute after this massaging action is begun, and sometimes the milk starts leaking from the
teats. At this moment, I lost no time in getting the milk out of the

udder. Once I started milking, I did not stop until the udder was completely emptied. Usually it required not more than five minutes to extract between thirty and forty pounds of milk from Inkie. This fast milking was very important because I knew that the hormone acted for about seven minutes only, after it was secreted into the blood stream, and that if a cow was not milked in that time, nothing on earth could get the rest of the milk from the cow. The cow was as helpless to accomplish this as the man in the moon. Thus, fast milking always produces more milk.

This remarkable truth about the actual process of milk secretion was discovered only recently by Dr. W. E. Petersen at the University of Minnesota, and explodes the old-fashioned theory that a cow produces milk while she is being milked and that she can hold up her milk. Milk is already manufactured inside a cow's udder before milking is started, and the cow has no control over letting down or holding up her milk. The action of the hormone controls the entire process. Any interference that excites a cow at milking time starts the secretion in the blood stream of a hormone, called adrenalin, which interferes with the action of the good hormone, oxytocin. Thus, it is shown why milkers that work with cows can be agents either for a complete letdown of milk or a holding up of milk.

Inkie was milked dry with a full hand wrapped around the teat, with the thumb outside. This correct way of milking prevents the inside of the teat canal from becoming injured, one of the main causes of mastitis and similar udder troubles. The fore quarters were invariably milked first, merely as a routine habit; since there is no evidence to indicate that the order in which quarters are milked makes the least bit of difference on the production of a cow. The idea that any milk from the rear quarters can be withdrawn through the fore quarters is absolutely wrong. Not a bit of milk produced in any one quarter can be drawn out of the other quarter. The cow's udder consists essentially of four separate glands, the arrangement of which differs from that in some other species of animal where they are widely separated. In the cow they are crowded together in such a way as to appear to be a unit.

After milking, the udder received another massaging, and last of all, Inkie received a grateful pat on the shoulder, and a gentle word of thanks. She turned her head around to me after each milking, expecting this little mark of appreciation.

The hot days of summer came while Inkie was producing so sensationally, and this was exactly what I had been dreading. The heat becomes very severe in this part of Iowa, and it is especially sultry down in the valley at Maytags where the cement roads around the barn draw the heat. Inkie had always suffered during the summer, and I realized I should have to take measures to counteract this trouble, and so tide her over the hot months.

The first thing I did every morning, then, was to clean her pen down to the cork-brick floor, and to soak it by turning the water hose on the floor. During the very hot days, I placed as little bedding on the floor as possible so the cow could lie close to the cool floor. In addition to the regular ceiling fan that was installed over every test cow, I placed a big electric fan directly in front of Inkie's box stall. Despite these two fans, the ton of cow puffed and breathed like a steam engine during the heat of the day. The reason for this will now be explained.

It has been shown that a cow that produces twenty pounds of milk a day exerts as much energy as a horse that works in the field all day long. Inkie was milking up to 118 pounds a day!

The story of the workings in the cow's udder is a very involved one, and highly technical. That the cow's udder is the hardest working tissue found anywhere in the animal kingdom is supported by some very well-established facts. First, all the major ingredients in milk are synthesized or manufactured in the cells lining the cow's udder. These milk substances that are made in the gland are lactose, casein, butterfat, and albumen. In addition to that, large amounts of work are performed in the selection of certain mineral elements out of the blood and building them up to much higher concentrations in the milk. For instance, calcium, on an average, is about seventeen times as concentrated in the milk as in the blood. Phosphorous is about the same, potassium about eight times, sugar about eighty times, and fat about twenty times. This requires considerable work, physiologically speaking, to effect such concentrations. Other forms of work are performed in keeping certain blood ingredients out of the milk entirely or partially. Among those are sodium bicarbonate or common baking soda which is not permitted to enter the milk at all. The chief salt of blood, sodium chloride, or our ordinary salt, is attained to less than one-seventh the amount in milk that is found in blood.

When Inkie was milking up to 118 pounds of milk in a day, the amount of work required to do that job was enormous. As an illustration of just one phase of the work required, that of pumping blood, the following explanation will suffice. About four hundred pounds of blood are pumped through the udder for each pound of milk produced, making for Inkie the staggering sum of over twenty-three tons of blood pumped through her udder in one day, to say nothing of the increased circulation required for other organs of the body in doing that job. Compared to physical labor, it is equal to the job that would be done in loading, let's say, twenty tons of coal onto a wagon over five feet high.

It is reasonable to believe that the harder a cow works, the more her system is liable to be affected by any sudden change or disturbance. I watched Inkie day and night for any possible upset. She had an iron constitution, yet I lived every hour dreading that something might happen to ruin the splendid record she was making. A thousand things could happen. She might fall into the creek again. She could develop a twisted intestine like that which had cut short the great record Amy would have made. Inkie might go along without mishap for ten months or longer; then some little thing, even an infected quarter in her udder, might throw her off at the end of the stretch.

Only once during her entire record was I away from Inkie for more than a few hours, and that time was during the Curtiss Candy Classic Sale held in June, 1946. I dreaded leaving her, but we were consigning to that sale the best bull calf that had ever left the Maytag herd to grace a consignment sale, and I felt duty bound to go with the calf.

The sale was to be held on June 3 in the spacious sale auditorium at Curtiss Candy Farm at Cary, Illinois. The Friday before the sale, a truck from Grinnell, Iowa, was hired to take the bull to Cary, and I accompanied the animal, together with the necessary feed and equipment.

When we arrived at the farm late in the evening, Jock McCormack was waiting for me, and helped me unload and get settled for the night. The calf was watered and fed a light feed, then allowed to rest after the long trip.

Most of the animals were in their places in one end of the huge amphitheater. Al Hay was in charge of the Carnation consignment, headed by Carnation Homestead Violet, a great matron that was hailed as "Queen of the West," and later topped the females in the sale at $12,500. I had met Mr. Hay several times before at different sales, and the first time I met him, I had been attracted by the easy, quiet way he worked with the animals in his charge. I remarked several times that he was one of the most typical cowmen I had ever seen. The Knutson boys from Wisconsin were there with their pleasant buffoonery; Sylvester Weiler, the very capable and likable herdsman from Pabst Farms, known by all merely as "Silver," was also on hand. Inimitable Joe Gemmeke from Clyde Hill Farms was with the gang, and with the presence of Merle Howard of Mooseheart, without whom no sale was complete, a lively and interesting time was inevitable.

The weather had turned bitterly cold for that season of the year, and I was tired after the trip, so I decided to retire for the night. Jock was put out of his bed in the house to make room for guests; so he came out to bunk with the men in the dormitory especially arranged to accommodate the men with the cattle. Jock and I reminisced over old times at Maytags for several hours before we both finally fell asleep. Several times during the night I was awakened by the laughing of some of the men below as they became a bit noisy in their game of penny ante.

The following morning, Saturday, was a busy day for the boys. The animals had to be washed and blanketed so that they would not catch cold. There was some clipping to be done that had been overlooked by some of the men at home. Horns had to be rasped and polished. And so the forenoon passed. Additional entries arrived during the day to bring the total number to fifty head.

Sunday was "prevue" day. The weather had fortunately moderated, and by noon the throng that had gathered for the gala occasion was immense. In the afternoon the animals were paraded outside before the seated crowd, and Glenn Householder, Extension Director for the Holstein-Friesian Association of America, gave a brief pedigree of each animal as it passed in review. As I led my bull past the center of the ring, the voice of Mr. Householder boomed out:

"Here comes the great Maytag bull, Maytag Ormsby Fobes Dictator. He is a double grandson of their great Dictator, and out of the great Pontiac family that produced Winterthur's famous 14th. This bull that Maytags are consigning is the richest Ormsby-bred young sire available in the country today!"

A feature of the Classic was the pool on the sale average, which grew to astronomical proportions. With each guess a dollar was placed in the pool, and the person coming nearest to the correct average

the sale would bring was to get the money. The jackpot amounted to
$210 after all the guesses were in. My own guess was slightly over
$3,000. The highest averaging sale to date was set at St. Paul in 1920
which averaged $3,075. The management of the first Curtiss Candy
Classic was attempting to top this average sale figure and set a new
record for the breed. To do this, they had personally selected animals
from the top herds of the United States and Canada, allowing but
seven males to be entered in the sale, with the remaining forty-three
animals to be females.

Prospective buyers passed up and down the aisles back of the sale
animals throughout Sunday afternoon; they jammed the barn on
Monday morning, asking questions about the different animals, including records, and so on. Mel Campbell remained near our consignment to handle his usual large share of the crowd that gathered
around the splendid black bull we were selling.

A white curtain was stretched across the length of the barn to
separate the fifty head from the main arena where the animals were
to be sold. The auditorium was decorated more beautifully perhaps
than at any sale that was ever held; the sale ring itself was especially
magnificent. Pure white shavings were strewn heavily on the raised
platform; artificial grass formed a natural bank down to the main
floor. On this grass, at intervals, were placed potted plants of red
geraniums. Across the auctioneer's box were written in artistic green
lettering the words: Curtiss Candy Classic. Above the box, a huge
American flag was draped in all its red, white, and blue glory.
Throughout the sale, free lunch was served. It was observed that Mrs.
Otto Schnering, wife of the farm's owner, assisted the help in serving
pie and sandwiches to the hungry sale goers.

One of the auctioneers at this sale was lovable Gene Mack. With
his ready wit and humor, coupled with the spontaneous tricks of magic
which he performed in the sale rings, there will never be another like
him.

The sale made history all right. The average was $3,082.50 for the
fifty head, the highest averaging sale in the history of the breed. The
Maytag bull was the second highest priced bull in the sale at $7,000.
Today Dictator is the most popular bull in Indiana, being used extensively by artificial insemination in many herds. He is regarded as one
of the greatest living sires of the breed. His own dam, Dictator Fobes
Pontiac Lass, is considered one of the greatest of the Holstein brood

cows. She was a member of the All-American "Produce" in 1948, and at the Maytag dispersal sale in 1949 brought $4,000.

Back from this great sale, I found Inkie well and still milking over a hundred pounds a day. She had dropped a few pounds from her high level, but she gained it back after a few days. From this time until the finish of her record, I did not leave her for a single milking.

By the end of the year, Inkie had made her thousand pounds of butterfat, and had till March 1, 1947, yet to run. The state record was held by a purebred Holstein, Montvic Rag Apple Bonheur Abbekerk, with 1,047 pounds of fat. This record had stood for a good many years, and I had hopes of breaking it in addition to making the 1,000-pound-fat record I had set out to do.

I had been told by a few cowmen that I should feed Inkie to the limit with grain and concentrates to get every pound that I could get out of her, even if it meant ruining her. She was getting old and the fact that she had a son to use in the herd or sell for a big figure would justify this action. But I should have counted the record a failure if to get it I should have to ruin the cow I had now become deeply attached to. Inkie never missed one feeding throughout her record, an unusual fact when it is understood that such cows are fed tremendous amounts of feed. But I was relying on roughage to achieve the results I was expecting.

On March 1, Inkie finished her record, still milking enough to furnish milk for an oyster supper served to the entire Maytag organization honoring the great event. Official figures came by air-mail a few days after the record was closed, establishing the record made by Inkie as the highest ever made in the state of Iowa on three milkings a day, regardless of age or breed. The exact production figures are: 27,499 pounds milk; 1,071.3 pounds fat; 3.9 per cent test. In terms of butter this would be over 1,300 pounds. Compared with the average production of United States dairy cows, according to the Department of Agriculture figures, of 4,500 pounds milk per year and 180 pounds fat per year, Inkie's record is stupendous and still stands in Iowa. She has also proved herself a great transmitting cow. She has a daughter and granddaughter living today in the Manning Creamery Company herd at Manning, Iowa. Both are classified "Excellent" and are called two of the greatest cows of the breed. A granddaughter, Mancryco Royal Rue, is one of the best show cows in Iowa.

A few days after Inka Rue's record was officially announced, Bill

Diamond, the associate farm editor of radio station WHO, devoted his fifteen-minute morning program to the story of this record performance.

At the end of her record, Inkie was in better condition than when she began her lactation; she was safe with calf, and was to go on to make another sensational record of 988 pounds of fat; she was further to astound everyone but me when, at eleven years of age, she was classified Very Good. No one could make fun of her appearance any more; not even Jock would be able to repeat what he had always said of her: "She isn't much to look at, but she can milk!"

☆ XX ☆

Daydreams

IT WAS SPRING again at Maytag Dairy Farms. The buds on the trees were bursting into green, the grass in the valley and on the hills was growing lush, and the tiny stream ran cool and clear in the pasture. Again the test cows were turned out on the grass, and they made an unforgettable picture as they grazed contentedly in this enchanted valley, with its gleaming white buildings under their green roofs in the background.

And as the evening closed about the world, the cows left the grass in the small yard near the barn and walked slowly, single file, up the hill, searching for deeper forage beyond.

On my way home one evening about this time, I stopped my car on the ridge overlooking the Maytag farm — the same spot that E. H. Maytag had so loved — and walked over to the fence along the pasture to watch the cows as they made their way up the crooked cow path. It was not often that I had the time now to stop to daydream, but it was good to daydream.

The cows saw me by the fence and started walking toward me, curious to see what I was doing there. Colantha reached her long tongue across the fence in gesture for a hand out. I was not likely to forget her, for she had just made over 800 pounds of fat — my first 800-pound-fat record. Princess was not far behind. She had just finished a record of over 740 pounds of fat made at past twelve years of age! I wondered what might have happened to her way back in those days when she was about to be sent to the block because of her unruly disposition, before faith and love had made her what she had become.

One cow remained behind the herd, and continued grazing in the valley by the creek. I watched her from a distance with immeasurable pride pulsing within me. The shadows of evening deepened.

Perhaps it was this magic time of day when light fades into dusk; perhaps a tear had momentarily clouded my vision, a tear over so many things that reminded me of yesterday — whatever it was, I cannot tell, but through this magic vista I saw another cow, familiar now as before. She was eating in a luscious pasture. The water in the stream was the purest I had ever seen, and the skies overhead the bluest I had ever beheld. It was the little pasture outside of Rockwell. A boy came running through the tall, lush grass toward the cow. He was barefooted and carried a green willow switch in his hand. There was a bulge in his patched overall pocket that might have been caused by a big red apple. He called in a familiar voice,

"Cutie! Cutie!"

The heifer stopped eating and looked up. As she recognized the boy, she turned and walked to meet him.

Epilogue

IT IS NOT an easy task to write a few last words to a story that for me ended some five years ago; events since that time are too recent to be viewed with any degree of objectivity, and would, even if they bore any direct relation to the narrative already told, assume the proportions of another volume if I consciously tried to draw them up from the Deep Well — which I do not choose to do. But Time does have its way, and Change asserts itself. A few incidents bearing heavily upon the historic nature of this tale will need to be recorded here.

The dispersal of the Maytag herd in the fall of 1949 came as a climax after more than thirty years of breeding fine cattle. The first distant rumblings of such an actuality were traceable as far back as 1940. E. H. Maytag, in his deep devotion to his own herd and to the Holstein breed as a whole, had hoped and planned for its continuance after his death. It is a fact, however, that human plans, no matter how carefully laid, are often thwarted.

Burdens and misfortunes, at times seemingly impossible to cope with, were met one by one in the ensuing years, and the Maytag herd blazed on. The death of Elmer Maytag in 1940 at once shifted the policy of the herd from that of a hobby to a strictly business basis. This change was thrust upon Mel Campbell, the farm's manager, at a time when he was laid up in a hospital with a serious back injury that had threatened to leave him paralyzed for life. To meet this challenge, a new product — Maytag Blue Cheese — was developed, and this business, an entirely different one, had to be mastered thoroughly from the ground up.

The blow that came very nearly being a mortal one for the herd struck in the form of a Bang's outbreak, and many of the very greatest animals of the famous herd were slaughtered before the management realized that something drastic would have to be done quickly to save it. Reactors to the disease were saved and quarantined on an isolation farm for the duration of their lives, while a program of calfhood vaccination got under way. And then came World War II, with its serious labor problems.

The Maytag herd recovered from all these setbacks and continued to make history. The very policies, however, at the core of the building of the herd — Advanced Registry testing, Big-Time showing, the best advertising and publicity of any Holstein herd in North America, and better-than-average salaries for specialized employees — were unpopular with several members of the Board of Directors. It must be remembered that the heirs of E. H. Maytag unfortunately failed to share his enthusiasm for the herd, both a serious yet pardonable handicap to the herd's success. As one of them remarked, "It is difficult or almost impossible for a man to acquire another man's hobby."

Several suggestions were offered and rejected, discontinuance of the isolation herd and a partial dispersal being the most seriously considered. Finally, even reluctantly by those least enthusiastic about the herd, a complete dispersal seemed the best and only solution. Accordingly, all efforts from June 1, 1949, were directed to the final ringing down of the curtain in a manner befitting one of the most colorful herds in the Holstein breed. Outside of two bulls that were being retained to head a commercial herd that Maytags planned to build later on, only two cows of any importance were kept out of the sale: Inka Rue Ollie Posch and Princess Ormsby Marathon Bessie.

Not since the great Dunloggin dispersal in 1943 had there been such interest in a Holstein sale. A week before the event, the entire herd, numbering 143 head, was removed to the Iowa State Fair Grounds at Des Moines, where facilities were more adequate for the handling of such a sale. On October 31 and November 1 more than 1,500 prospective buyers from nearly every state were on hand to witness the sale that averaged $1,038.

Radio Station KXEL, Waterloo, had a direct wire hookup to the sale and broadcast the first fifteen minutes of the proceedings. The crowd was informed of the intense Ormsby background of the herd, and the fact was pointed out that only three animals in the entire offering carried less than three crosses to Sir Pietertje Ormsby Mercedes.

Maytag Ormsby Pontiac Josephine, famous seven-year-old show daughter of Dictator from the 918-pound De Kol Aaltje Pontiac Lass 2d herself (foundation cow of Maytag's most illustrious cow family — the Pontiacs), was the top animal of the sale at $4,500, going to Harold Goldsmith of Ridgefield, Connecticut, who was the highest single buyer in the sale, taking nineteen head for a total of nearly $36,000. Maytag Ormsby Fobes Olive, the most popular daughter of her Gold Medal sire, Maytag Ormsby Fobes, was purchased for $3,400 by Dr. Joseph Pape of Chicago. Olive was later classified "Excellent." Of the 143 head sold, only 15 stayed in the state of Iowa; the geography of the dispersal showed a total of 56 buyers from 15 states. Of the total offering, 46 brought four-figure prices.

The public interest in the Maytag herd evidenced at this sale, together with the appeal made by the animals themselves in the sale ring, made a deep impression on Fred Maytag. Who can say it was not the tiny seed planted at this time that may lead to the blossoming of a new and greater purebred herd at Maytags in the near future, instead of merely the commercial herd originally planned?

The Maytag dispersal broke another link in the chain of my life

connected directly with dairy cattle. There followed three terms of
teaching school again, this time in Jasper County. Then, more recently, there were two years back with Holsteins once more, at the
renowned Clyde Hill Farms in Missouri — and now the hope of returning to Iowa.

There is little more to be said in tribute to the purebred Holstein
cow; it is not easy for everyone to recognize her worth as I do. The
years of wartime prosperity are over. Agriculture now faces many
serious problems. For the dairy farmer there is the threat of milk,
butter, and butterfat substitutes flooding the market; the reduction
in the price of milk due to surpluses, while at the same time the cost
of milk production remains high; and the decrease of purebred bull
sales brought on by the rapid development of artificial insemination.

As a result, the challenge to the purebred dairy cow has never
been greater while at the same time it is doubtful that the position of
the Holstein cow has ever been stronger in the history of the great
breed than it is today. There is every reason to believe the Holstein
industry can adopt the philosophy of accelerated adaptability in the
changing demand of both dairy products and seed-stock. The Holstein cow is preeminently the cow of amazing production ability, and
today, with an increasing American population demanding less and
less fat in its diet, the black and white cow with its perfect balance of
low fats and high percentage of milk solids stands alone. And because she is able to convert roughages into milk more economically
than any other of the dairy breeds, the Holstein can and will survive
in an age of change. It is to be hoped there are few purebred Holstein
herds maintained for the sole purpose of selling a few bull calves; a
registered herd of Holsteins can mean so much more and has so much
more to offer the genuine breeder.

What has been written throughout these pages has been in praise
of the purebred Holstein cow in particular, but what I really should
like it to be is a tribute to the dairy cow in general. Her place in liter-
ature is meager; her services to mankind can never be fully realized
or rewarded. Her only monument is the billions of men, women, and
children who have been nourished from the dawn of history by the
milk from this ever docile, contented servant of man.

It is easy for one who likes dairy cows to grow poetic, as did Robert
Louis Stevenson in his "The friendly cow all red and white, I love
with all my might," or as did Thomas Gray in the simple, poignant

opening lines of his immortal "Elegy": "The lowing herd winds slowly o'er the lea . . . And leaves the world to darkness and to me."

There is need today in a world of harsh realities for moments of fancy, for dreams; I chose to end the final chapter of this book on such a note. But since this is an age of truth and not fiction, since Americans are essentially a truth-seeking people, I have presented only facts in these last few pages. For, as Winston Churchill once said, "Facts are better than dreams."